Algebra Tools

Algebra

BRITANNICA
Mathematics in Context

TEACHER'S GUIDE

HOLT, RINEHART AND WINSTON

Mathematics in Context is a comprehensive curriculum for the middle grades. It was developed in 1991 through 1997 in collaboration with the Wisconsin Center for Education Research, School of Education, University of Wisconsin-Madison and the Freudenthal Institute at the University of Utrecht, The Netherlands, with the support of the National Science Foundation Grant No. 9054928.

The revision of the curriculum was carried out in 2003 through 2005, with the support of the National Science Foundation Grant No. ESI 0137414.

National Science Foundation

Opinions expressed are those of the authors and not necessarily those of the Foundation.

Kindt, M.; Dekker, T.; Burrill, G.; and Romberg, T. (2006). *Algebra tools.* In Wisconsin Center for Education Research and Freudenthal Institute (Eds.), *Mathematics in context.* Chicago: Encyclopaedia Britannica.

The Teacher's Guide for this unit was prepared by David C. Webb, Teri Hedges, Margaret R. Meyer, Thomas A. Romberg, Truus Dekker, and Monica Wijers.

ISBN 0-03-040429-0

2 3 4 5 6 073 09 08 07 06

The *Mathematics in Context* Development Team

Development 2003–2005

Algebra Tools was developed by Martin Kindt and Truus Dekker. It was adapted for use in American schools by Gail Burrill and Thomas A. Romberg.

Wisconsin Center for Education

Research Staff

Thomas A. Romberg
Director

David C. Webb
Coordinator

Gail Burrill
Editorial Coordinator

Margaret A. Pligge
Editorial Coordinator

Project Staff

Sarah Ailts
Beth R. Cole
Erin Hazlett
Teri Hedges
Karen Hoiberg
Carrie Johnson
Jean Krusi
Elaine McGrath

Margaret R. Meyer
Anne Park
Bryna Rappaport
Kathleen A. Steele
Ana C. Stephens
Candace Ulmer
Jill Vettrus

Freudenthal Institute Staff

Jan de Lange
Director

Truus Dekker
Coordinator

Mieke Abels
Content Coordinator

Monica Wijers
Content Coordinator

Arthur Bakker
Peter Boon
Els Feijs
Dédé de Haan
Martin Kindt

Nathalie Kuijpers
Huub Nilwik
Sonia Palha
Nanda Querelle
Martin van Reeuwijk

Contents

Contents

◆ Introduction

Introduction

The *Algebra Tools* are extra practice and extension problems for the Algebra strand. Some of the problems go beyond typical content goals for middle grades mathematics. These problems are designed as challenge problems and extension activities for students who are motivated to explore advanced topics in algebra.

Two resources are offered for Algebra Tools: a teacher guide with black line masters that can be photocopied for student use, and a consumable student workbook. In the teacher guide resource, blackline masters appear on the left-hand pages in this book. Opposite them, on the right-hand pages, are solutions for teacher use. Some practice activities run longer than one page; in those instances, they are continued on the following left hand page.

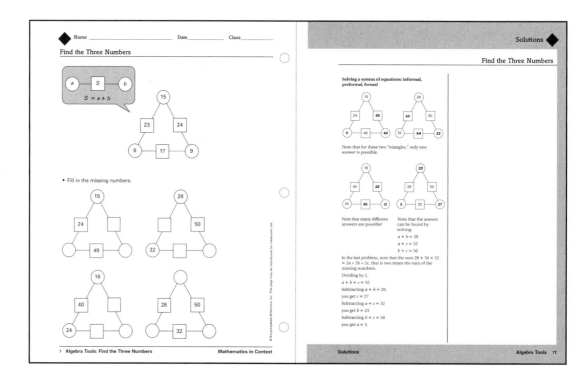

This resource follows the learning lines from the *Mathematics in Context* grade 6 through 8 algebra units, but can be used independently from this curriculum. There is no implied order to the sections or the pages within each section as long as the topic addressed has been adequately introduced. Activities can be completed in class or assigned as homework whenever you feel that your class needs extra practice or review.

Overview

The traditional way of practicing algebra is to complete long rows of exercises that do not provide any additional challenge. Guenther Malle, in the German publication, *Didaktische Probleme der elementaren Algebra* (1993), says that every teacher finds out sooner or later that the "exercise ideology" yields relatively little result and if there is some positive result, it is short-lived. Building skills, however, is not enough. Students should also build understanding and insight. Most of the exercises in the *Algebra Tools* cannot be completed by simply using recall or rote knowledge. These exercises might be considered a type of "principled practice," in which students are required to reason and demonstrate understanding of algebra.

There is a wide a variety in the presentation of the exercises: arrow strings, operation trees, number strips, charts, and so on. Here is one example from the book:

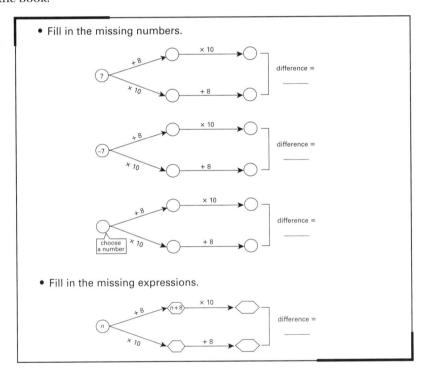

This example, in a nutshell, shows how students go through a process of informal to formal reasoning. In this sense it is rather representative for the style of the exercises in this book. First students find, while working with numbers, how a change in the order of operations influences the outcome. A nice extension here could be to ask students to describe a problem context to support this situation, where it makes sense for the difference to be independent of the input number. As students work through the exercises, they prove the rule using expressions instead of numbers. In general, it's a good idea to let the students produce their own examples. In this case (and in many other questions of this book!), it's also possible to ask the students to design a similar exercise. This principle of asking students to make their own problems is usually very fruitful because of the reflection involved and the need to understand underlying principles at play in the structure of the series of problems.

Introduction

The philosophy of "principled practice" used in the MiC units as well as in *Algebra Tools* means that students start by exploring concepts using numbers (informal stage), begin to see patterns in these numbers (preformal stage), and are motivated to represent problems using variables (formal stage). On the MiC website, mic.hrw.com, applets for additional practice also can be found: e.g., Tic Tac Go, Arrow Strings and Solving Equations with the balance strategy.

Mathematics Content Addressed in *Algebra Tools*

As students work with the *Algebra Tools*, they will practice:

- solving a system of equations;
  - Students use informal, preformal and formal strategies.
- solving linear equations, both simple and complex;
  - Students use different strategies: Difference is zero, Cover method, Balance method.
- solving quadratic equations (informal and preformal) where variables represent positive whole numbers;
- finding patterns in numbers;
  - Students use many different worksheets where they work at an informal and preformal level.
  - Students relate the patterns in numbers to formulas and equations.
  - Students explore geometric representations of numbers (triangular, square, and rectangular patterns).
- building formulas and equations for linear relationships;
  - Students use patterns in numbers to build formulas.
  - Students explore the relationship between equation, table, and graph.
- building simple quadratic formulas and equations;
  - Students use patterns in numbers to build formulas.
  - Students relate the patterns in numbers to quadratic formulas.
- using a coordinate system;
  - Students use the concepts of slope, x-intercept, and y-intercept of straight lines and the relationship between them.
  - Students draw graphs and check calculated intersection points.
  - Students explore the relationship between parallel lines and their equations.
  - Students transform figures on a grid.
- using order of operations and the distributive, commutative, and associative properties, with numbers as well as variables;
  - Students combine similar terms, add and subtract expressions, and multiply an expression by a number informally, preformally, and formally.
  - Students show flexibility in operations with expressions and equations.
  - Students recognize equivalent expressions and formulas.

- operating with integers; and
  - Students make computations with integers informally, preformally, and formally.
  - Students understand rules for computations with integers.
- using symbolic language and algebra rules.
  - Students "translate" text in words into symbolic language.
  - Students make informal and preformal use of rules $(a - b)(a + b) = a^2 - b^2$ and $(a + b)^2 = a^2 + 2ab + b^2$.
  - Students make calculations with exponents preformally and formally.
  - Students show flexibility in working with powers.
  - In a preformal and formal way, students perform operations with fractions containing numbers as well as variables.

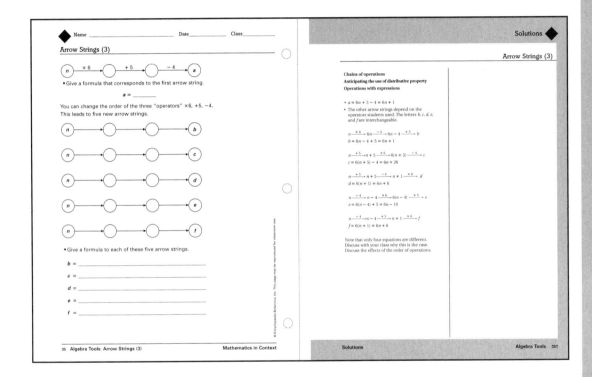

Name _____ Date _____ Class _____

Comparing Prices (2)

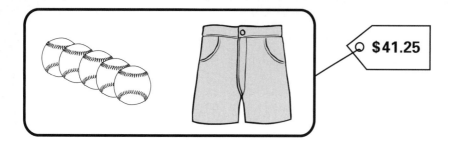

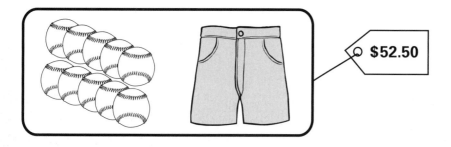

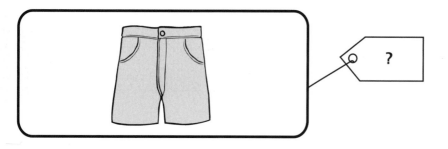

• Show your work.

Solving a system of equations: informal, preformal

Answer: One pair of shorts costs $30.

Student work will vary. Sample student work:

- Five tennis balls and one pair of shorts cost $41.25

  Ten tennis balls and one pair of shorts cost $52.50

  So five tennis balls cost $52.50 − $41.25 = $11.25

  One pair of shorts costs $41.25 − $11.25 = $30

- $5B + 1S = 41.25$

  $10B + 1S = 52.50$

  subtracting both equations results in:

  $5B = 11.25$

  (One ball costs $11.25 ÷ 5 = $2.25, but this answer was not asked for.)

  $1S = 41.25 − 11.25 = 30$

  or

  $10B = 2 × 11.25 = 22.50$

  $1S = 52.50 − 22.50 = 30$

Comparing Weights

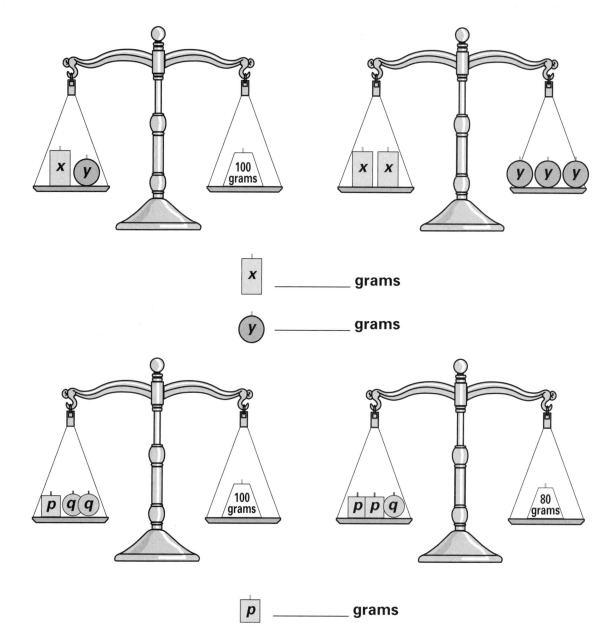

x _____ grams

y _____ grams

p _____ grams

q _____ grams

Solving a system of equations: preformal

Note that students may use a more informal way of reasoning to find the answers!

First Set:

$x + y = 100$ $2x = 3y$

$2x + 2y = 200$ double $x + y = 100$

$3y + 2y = 200$ replace $2x$ with $3y$

$5y = 200$

$y = 40$ (gram)

$x = 60$ (gram)

Second Set:

One strategy for the second system of equations is:

$p + 2q = 100 \quad \downarrow (-20)$ For each p added and q subtracted, subtract 20 from the weight.

$2p + q = 80 \quad \downarrow (-20)$

$3p + 0q = 60$

$p = 20$ (gram) and $q = 40$ (gram)

Another Strategy:

$p + 2q = 100$ add both equations

$\underline{2p + q = 80}$

$3p + 3q = 180$ divide by three

$\underline{p + q = 60}$

$p + 2q = 100$ subtract

$\underline{ p + q = 60}$

$q = 40$ (gram)

$p = 20$ (gram)

Comparing Lengths

There are four pieces of rope. Three pieces have the same length; the fourth one is longer than the other three.

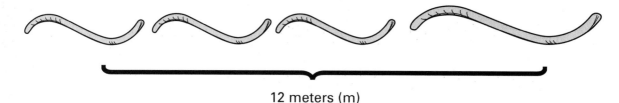

12 meters (m)

All the pieces together are 12 m.

One short and one long piece together are 7 m.

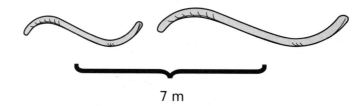

7 m

• What is the length of one short piece of rope? One long piece? Show your work.

Another rope, with a length of 18 m, is cut in 5 pieces.

Two pieces are equal in length. The other three pieces are equal in length, but they are shorter than the first two.

One short and one long piece are 8 m together.

• What is the length of one short piece of rope? One long piece? Show your work.

Solving a system of equations,: informal, preformal

Answer: One short piece of rope is $2\frac{1}{2}$ meters or 2.5 meters long.

One long piece of rope is $4\frac{1}{2}$ meters or 4.5 meters long.

Sample student work:

- In the first drawing, I can exchange one short and one long piece for seven meters. Two short pieces are $12 - 7 = 5$ meters long; each is $5 \div 2 = 2\frac{1}{2}$ meters or 2.5 meters long. One long piece is $7 - 2\frac{1}{2} = 4\frac{1}{2}$ meters or 4.5 meters long.

- $3S + 1L = 12$

  $1S + 1L = 7$

  subtracting both equations results in:

  $2S = 5$

  $S = \frac{5}{2} = 2\frac{1}{2}$

  $L = 7 - 2\frac{1}{2} = 4\frac{1}{2}$

Answer: One short piece of rope is 2 meters long.

One long piece of rope is 6 meters long.

Student work will vary. Sample student work:

- Two long pieces plus three short pieces are 18 meters long.

  One short and one long piece are 8 meters long.

  I can exchange two short pieces and two long pieces for 16 meters, leaving one short piece that is 2 meters long. One long piece of rope is $8 - 2 = 6$ meters long.

- $3S + 2L = 18$

  $1S + 1L = 8$

  Multiply the last equation by 2:

  $2S + 2L = 16$

  subtracting this equation from the first one results in:

  $1S = 2$

  $1L = 8 - 2 = 6$

Name _____ Date_____ Class_____

How Old?

together 54

together 21

together 51

Solving a system of equations: informal, preformal, formal

Answer: Mother is 42 years old; son is 12 years old; and daughter is 9 years old.

Sample student work:

- Look at the two pictures with the mother. You can see that the difference in age between son and daughter is three years. If you add their ages, the sum is 21. Now students may guess and check, for example, 10 and 11 or 9 and 12.

  Note: Guessing is sometimes a good strategy, but then you always need to check whether or not the answer fits the equation(s).

- $$\begin{array}{r} M + S = 54 \\ S + D = 21 \\ + \underline{\quad M + D = 51 \quad} \\ 2M + 2S + 2D = 126 \qquad \text{divide by 2} \\ M + S + D \quad = 63 \end{array}$$

  $$\begin{array}{r} M + S = 54 \\ - \underline{\quad M + D = 51 \quad} \\ S - D = 3 \end{array}$$

- $$\begin{array}{r} M + S + D = 63 \\ - \underline{\quad M + S \quad\quad = 21 \quad} \\ D = 9; \ S = 12; \ M = 42 \end{array}$$

  $$\begin{array}{r} S + D = 21 \\ + \underline{\quad S - D = 3 \quad} \\ 2S = 24 \\ S = 12; \ D = 21 - 12 = 9 \\ M = 54 - 12 = 42 \end{array}$$

How Long?

Three pieces of rope

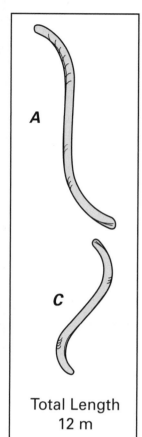

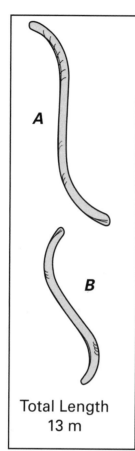

A

C

Total Length
12 m

A

B

Total Length
13 m

B

C

Total Length
10 m

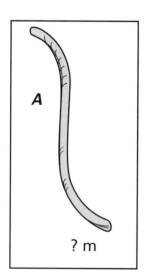

A

? m

B

? m

C

? m

Solving a system of equations: preformal, formal

Answer: $A = 7\frac{1}{2}$; $B = 5\frac{1}{2}$; $C = 4\frac{1}{2}$

Sample student work:

- Look at the second and third picture. You can see the difference between A and C is three meters. The sum of A and C is 12 meters. Adding the difference and the sum of A and C results in $2A = 15$; $A = 7\frac{1}{2}$

$$C = 12 - 7\frac{1}{2} = 4\frac{1}{2}$$
$$B = 10 - 4\frac{1}{2} = 5\frac{1}{2}$$

- $$A + B = 13$$
$$- \underline{B + C = 10}$$
$$A - C = 3$$

$$A + C = 12$$
$$+ \underline{A - C = 3}$$
$$2A = 15 \quad A = \frac{15}{2} = 7\frac{1}{2}$$
$$C = 12 - 7\frac{1}{2} = 4\frac{1}{2}$$
$$B = 10 - 4\frac{1}{2} = 5\frac{1}{2}$$

- $$2A + 2B + 2C = 12 + 13 + 10 = 35$$

divide by 2 $\quad A + B + C = 17\frac{1}{2}$
$$- \underline{A + B = 13}$$
$$C = 4\frac{1}{2};$$
$$B = 10 - 4\frac{1}{2} = 5\frac{1}{2};$$
$$A = 7\frac{1}{2}$$

Find the Three Numbers

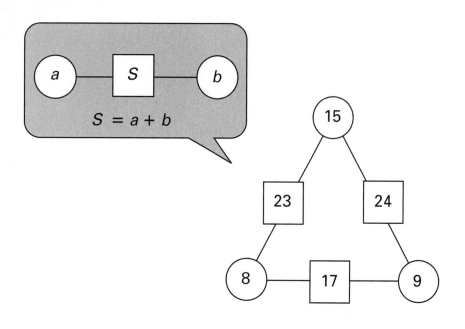

- Fill in the missing numbers.

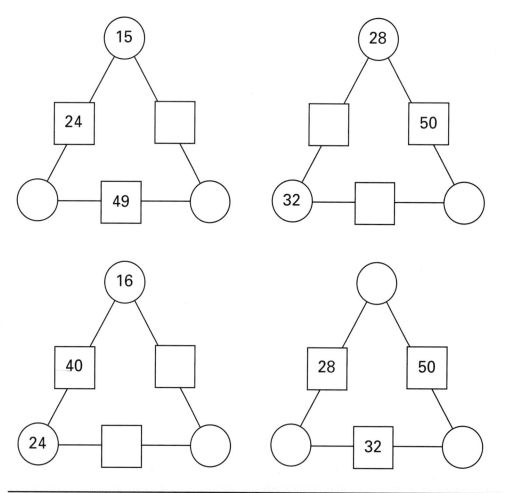

Mathematics in Context

Solving a system of equations: informal, preformal, formal

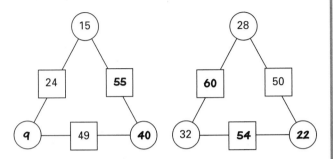

Note that for these two "triangles," only one answer is possible.

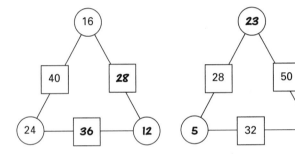

Note that many different answers are possible for the above triangle.

Note that the answer can be found by solving:

$$a + b = 28$$
$$a + c = 32$$
$$b + c = 50$$

In the last problem, note that the sum $28 + 50 + 32 = 2a + 2b + 2c$, that is two times the sum of the missing numbers.

Dividing by 2,

$a + b + c = 55$

Subtracting $a + b = 28$,

you get $c = 27$

Subtracting $a + c = 32$

you get $b = 23$

Subtracting $b + c = 50$

you get $a = 5$.

Find the Missing Numbers

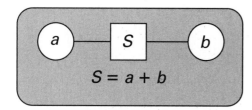

$$S = a + b$$

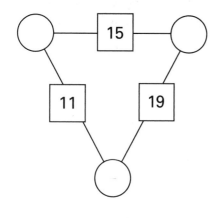

- There is only one solution. Which one?

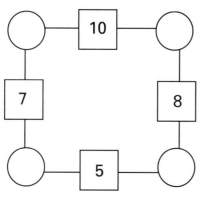

- There are a lot of solutions!

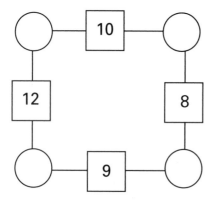

- This doesn't work! Explain why not.

Solving a system of equations: preformal, formal

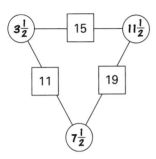

Note that the answer can be found by solving:

$a + b = 15$

$a + c = 11$

$b + c = 19$

In this problem, note that the sum $15 + 11 + 19$ is two times the sum of the missing number (See the solution on the previous page.)

Here is one example of a solution for the second problem using a negative whole number. Students should be able to show why more than one solution is possible.

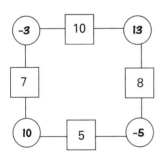

Note that $10 + 5 = 7 + 8$.

For the last problem, a sample reasoning could be:

- In the previous problem, if you added the horizontal numbers, you found that

   $10 + 5 = 7 + 8$. In this problem, $10 + 9 \neq 12 + 8$, which is the reason why this one does not work:

   $10 + 9$ is the sum of four missing numbers.

   $12 + 8$ is the sum of four missing numbers.

   $20 \neq 19$, so there cannot be a solution for this problem.

- If you want to find a solution, you have to solve these equations:

   $a + b = 10 \qquad b + d = 8$

   $a + c = 12 \qquad c + d = 9$

   Subtracting the two sets of equations leads to:

   $b - c = -2$ and $b - c = 1$. These equations cannot both be true, so there is no solution to the fourth problem.

Sum and Product (1)

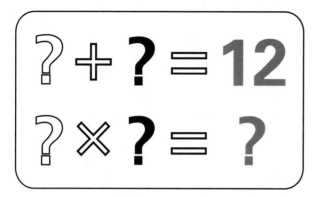

There are two positive integers. If you add both numbers, the result will be 12.

- What are the results if you multiply the integers?
  Show all the results you found.

Finding patterns

Anticipating use of variables

The results are 11; 20; 27; 32; 35; 36

$1 + 11 = 12$	$1 \times 11 = 11$
$2 + 10 = 12$	$2 \times 10 = 20$
$3 + 9 = 12$	$3 \times 9 = 27$
$4 + 8 = 12$	$4 \times 8 = 32$
$5 + 7 = 12$	$5 \times 7 = 35$
$6 + 6 = 12$	$6 \times 6 = 36$

Sum and Product (2)

$$6 + 14 = 20 \qquad 6 \times 14 = 84$$

| **Sum** of 6 and 14 | **Product** of 6 and 14 |

Two positive integers have a sum of 20.

If the numbers were 6 and 14, their product would be 84.

But there are other pairs of positive whole numbers whose sum is equal to 20 with products that are not 84.

Below you see a chart with numbers from 1 to 100.

- Color all the cells that show a product for two numbers that have a sum of 20.

1	2	3	4	5	6	7	8	9	10
11	12	13	14	15	16	17	18	19	20
21	22	23	24	25	26	27	28	29	30
31	32	33	34	35	36	37	38	39	40
41	42	43	44	45	46	47	48	49	50
51	52	53	54	55	56	57	58	59	60
61	62	63	64	65	66	67	68	69	70
71	72	73	74	75	76	77	78	79	80
81	82	83	84	85	86	87	88	89	90
91	92	93	94	95	96	97	98	99	100

- Write the results in a sequence from large to small.

- Do you see any pattern in this sequence? Describe the pattern you see.

Finding patterns

Anticipating use of variables

- The results, written as a sequence from large to small:

  19   36   51   64   75   84   91   96   99   100

- The difference between successive numbers becomes smaller:

  17   15   13   11   9   7   5   3   1

- The differences are odd numbers.

Note: The difference in the sequence of differences, sometimes called "second difference," is always two (e.g., $17 - 15 = 2$ and $15 - 13 = 2$).

Sum and Product (3)

Two positive whole numbers have a product equal to 24.

- What can their sum be?

Three positive whole numbers have a sum equal to 10.

- What can their product be?

Finding patterns

Anticipating use of variables

- $1 \times 24 = 24$ $1 + 24 = 25$

  $2 \times 12 = 24$ $2 + 12 = 14$

  $3 \times 8 = 24$ $3 + 8 = 11$

  $4 \times 6 = 24$ $4 + 6 = 10$

- $1 + 1 + 8 = 10$ $1 \times 1 \times 8 = 8$

  $1 + 2 + 7 = 10$ $1 \times 2 \times 7 = 14$

  $1 + 3 + 6 = 10$ $1 \times 3 \times 6 = 18$

  $1 + 4 + 5 = 10$ $1 \times 4 \times 5 = 20$

  $2 + 2 + 6 = 10$ $2 \times 2 \times 6 = 24$

  $2 + 3 + 5 = 10$ $2 \times 3 \times 5 = 30$

  $2 + 4 + 4 = 10$ $2 \times 4 \times 4 = 32$

  $3 + 3 + 4 = 10$ $3 \times 3 \times 4 = 36$

Sum and Product (4)

A and *B* represent positive whole numbers.

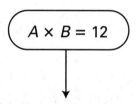

$A \times B =$ _____ or _____ or _____ or _____ or _____ or _____

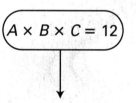

$A + B =$ _____ or _____ or _____

$A \times B \times C = 12$

$A + B + C =$ _____ or _____ or _____ or _____

Finding patterns: informal, preformal.

Using variables

$A \times B =$ _**11**_ or _**20**_ or _**27**_ or _**32**_ or _**35**_ or _**36**_

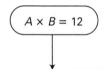

$A + B =$ _**7**_ or _**8**_ or _**13**_

$A \times B \times C = 12$

$A + B + C =$ _**7**_ or _**8**_ or _**9**_ or _**14**_

Sum and Difference (1)

> **Number Game**
> Think of a number less than 10. This is your starting number.
> Add 10 to your starting number.
> Also subtract your starting number from 10.
> Add both results. Which number do you get?
> Repeat this a few times with another starting number.

- What happens? How can you explain this?

Change the number 10 to 25 and play the same number game.
- What will the result be?

Finding patterns using opposite operations: informal

Anticipating use of variables.

Visual explanation

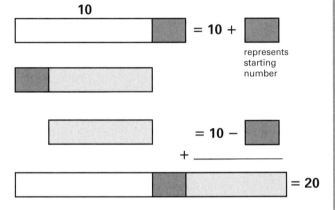

represents starting number

$+$ _____

Some examples with different starting numbers:

starting number 7 $10 + 7 = 17$

$+ \dfrac{10 - 7 = 3}{20}$

starting number 2 $10 + 2 = 12$

$+ \dfrac{10 - 2 = 8}{20}$

The result is always 20. Possible explanation:
If you add $(10 + 7)$ and $(10 - 7)$ you first have to
add 7 and then subtract 7. The result is you only
add 10 and 10.

If you change 10 to 25, the result will always be 50.

Sum and Difference (2)

The sum of two numbers is equal to 20.

If both numbers are equal, each of them is 10.

If the numbers are unequal, the bigger one is greater than 10.

So this number is **10 + *any number*** or **10 + *a*** for short.

• How can you write the smaller number for short?

Look at the number line.

The sum of two *unequal* numbers is 60.

The bigger number is indicated on the number line.

• Indicate the smaller number on the number line.

Be as accurate as you can.

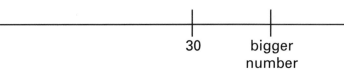

You know that the sum of two numbers is 100 and their difference is 12.

• Find these numbers.

You know that the sum of two numbers is 80 and their difference is 15.

• What are these numbers?

Informal use of variables

- The smaller number can be written $10 - a$.

- The smaller number should be indicated to the left of 30, at the same distance from 30 as the bigger number.

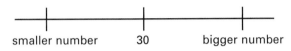

smaller number   30   bigger number

- The numbers are 56 and 44.

  You can write the numbers as $50 + a$ and $50 - a$.

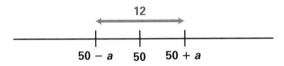

12

$50 - a$ 50 $50 + a$

Find the difference by using a number line or by subtracting:

$$\begin{array}{r} 50 + a \\ -\ \underline{50 - a} \\ 2a = 12 \\ a = 6 \end{array}$$

The numbers are $50 + 6 = 56$ and $50 - 6 = 44$.

Check that $56 - 44 = 12$ and $56 + 44 = 100$.

- The numbers are $47\frac{1}{2}$ and $32\frac{1}{2}$

  You can write the numbers as $40 + a$ and $40 - a$.

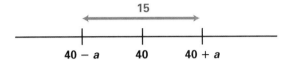

15

$40 - a$ 40 $40 + a$

Find the difference by using a number line or by subtracting:

$$\begin{array}{r} 40 + a \\ -\ \underline{40 - a} \\ 2a = 15 \\ a = 7\frac{1}{2} \end{array}$$

The numbers are $40 + 7\frac{1}{2} = 47\frac{1}{2}$ and $40 - 7\frac{1}{2} = 32\frac{1}{2}$

Check that $47\frac{1}{2} - 32\frac{1}{2} = 15$ and $47\frac{1}{2} + 32\frac{1}{2} = 100$

Different Differences (1)

Isabelle earned $100. She wants to buy a pair of running shoes. They normally cost $70. So she expects $30 will be left.

She is lucky! When she enters the shop, she discovers that the pair she wants is reduced by $8.

- How many dollars does she have left?

There are two ways to calculate this.

    a. $100 - (70 - 8)$

    b. $(100 - 70) + 8$

- Did you use method **a** or method **b**?
- Without looking at the result of the calculation, explain why the method you did not use would work just as well.

Suppose Isabelle already knew that the price of the shoes was reduced, but she did not know how much. So she knew that more than $30 should be left!

- Use the story to explain $100 - (70 - a) = 30 + a$.

A more general equality is $100 - (p - a) = 100 - p + a$.

- Explain this equality.

    (You may suppose $p < 100$ and $a < p$.)

A frequently occurring error is $100 - (p - a) = 100 - p - a$.

- Invent a short story in which someone has $100 - p - a$ left from 100 dollars instead of $100 - p$.
- Fill in the right expression: $100 - ($_____$) = 100 - p - a$.

Relating patterns in numbers to relations with variables

Anticipating subtraction of a binomial

- She will have $8 more than $30, so $38 dollars are left.

- In the example, the second method was used: First subtract 70 from 100 and then add 8.

- First subtracting 8 from 70 and then subtracting the result from 100 has the same effect.

- Isabelle knew the original price was $70 minus some amount of reduction, labeled a.

  So she knows she will have left $100 - 70 = 30$ plus the amount the price is reduced by.

- The equality just uses a general p for the original price. Look at the first equality and change 70 for p and 8 for a.

- Example story: Isabelle wants to buy a pair of shoes. They normally cost $70, so she expects $30 will be left. Unfortunately, she finds out the price was recently raised by $8, so she will have $30 - $8 left.

- $100 - (p + a) = 100 - p - a$

Different Differences (2)

If you subtract less, there will be more left.
Example:

$$50 - 20 = 30$$
$$50 - (20 - x) = 30 + x$$

If you subtract more, there will be less left.
- Invent an example.

- Here are four conclusions. The first one is complete.
  Explain that one.
- Complete the other three.

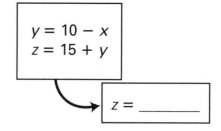

$$y = 10 - x$$
$$z = 15 - y$$
→ $z = 5 + x$

$$y = 10 - x$$
$$z = 15 + y$$
→ $z = $ _____

$$y = 10 + x$$
$$z = 15 + y$$
→ $z = $ _____

$$y = 10 + x$$
$$z = 15 - y$$
→ $z = $ _____

- Invent some other conclusions in the same style.
  Use symbols other than x, y, and z.

Showing flexibility in operations with expressions

Anticipating subtraction of a binomial

- One example: $100 - 80 = 20$
  $100 - (80 + 5) = 20 - 5$
  $100 - (80 + x) = 20 - x$

- First conclusion: In the second equation,
  replace y by $(10 - x)$
  $z = 15 - (10 - x) = 5 + x$

- Second conclusion: $z = 15 + (10 - x) = 25 - x$
  Third conclusion: $z = 15 + (10 + x) = 25 + x$
  Fourth conclusion: $z = 15 - (10 + x) = 5 - x$

- Conclusions will vary. Have students check each other's work.

Different Differences (3)

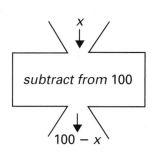 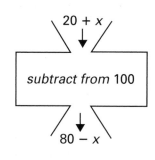 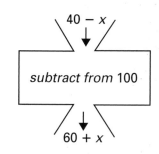

- The sum of INPUT and OUTPUT is 100 in each case. Check this out.
- Complete the chain.

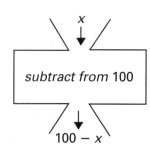

The chain on the left corresponds to the following chain of differences.

$$30 - [80 - (150 - (100 - x))] = \underline{\hspace{1cm}}$$

- This expression is equivalent to an expression with only one term. What is this expression?

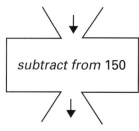

- Make chains corresponding to:

$$10 - (9 - (8 - y))$$
$$16 - [9 - (4 - (1 - a))]$$
$$32 - [16 - [8 - (4 - (2 - k))]]$$

- What are the three resulting expressions?

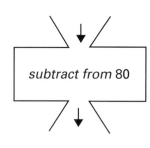

- Invent a "chain exercise" yourself. Provide an answer to it.

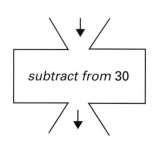

Equivalent expressions

Using parentheses in expressions

Adding each equation pair

$$+\begin{array}{c} x \\ \underline{100 - x} \\ 100 \end{array} \qquad +\begin{array}{c} 20 + x \\ \underline{80 - x} \\ 100 \end{array} \qquad +\begin{array}{c} 40 - x \\ \underline{60 + x} \\ 100 \end{array}$$

- The chain completed:

$x \xrightarrow{\textit{Subtract from 100}} 100 - x \xrightarrow{\textit{Subtract from 150}} 50 + x$
$\xrightarrow{\textit{Subtract from 80}} 30 - x \xrightarrow{\textit{Subtract from 30}} x$

- $30 - [80 - (150 - (100 - x))] = x$

- $10 - (9 - (8 - y) = 9 - y$
  $y \xrightarrow{\textit{Subtract from 8}} 8 - y \xrightarrow{\textit{Subtract from 9}} 1 + y$
  $\xrightarrow{\textit{Subtract from 10}} 9 - y$

- $16 - [9 - (4 - (1 - a))] = 10 + a$
  $a \xrightarrow{\textit{Subtract from 1}} 1 - a \xrightarrow{\textit{Subtract from 4}} 3 + a$
  $\xrightarrow{\textit{Subtract from 9}} 6 - a \xrightarrow{\textit{Subtract from 16}} 10 + a$

- $32 - [16 - [8 - (4 - (2 - k))]] = 22 - k$
  $k \xrightarrow{\textit{Subtract from 2}} 2 - k \xrightarrow{\textit{Subtract from 4}} 2 + k$
  $\xrightarrow{\textit{Subtract from 8}} 6 - k \xrightarrow{\textit{Subtract from 16}} 10 + k$
  $\xrightarrow{\textit{Subtract from 32}} 22 - k$

- Answer for question 5 is:
  $9 - y$
  $10 + a$
  $22 - k$

- Have students check each other's chain-exercises and answers.

Find the Value of *x* (1)

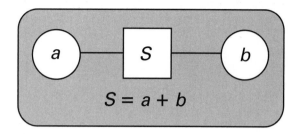

$$S = a + b$$

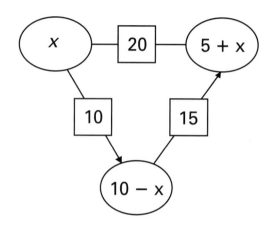

$x + 5 + x = 20$

$x =$ _____

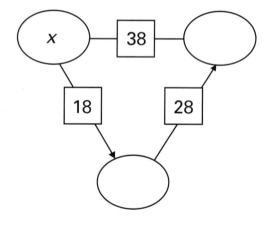

_____

$x =$ _____

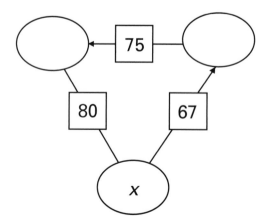

_____

$x =$ _____

Solving linear equations: informal, preformal.

$x = 7\frac{1}{2}$; $x = 14$; $x = 36$

Possible student work:

$x + 5 + x = 20 \quad x = 7\frac{1}{2}$

Note the direction of the arrows in the "triangles."

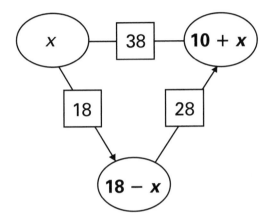

$$10 + x + x = 38$$
$$2x = 28$$
$$x = 14$$

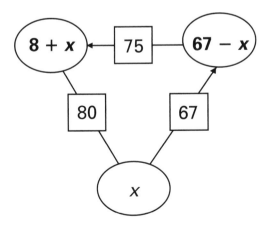

$$8 + x + x = 80$$
$$2x = 72$$
$$x = 36$$

Find the Value of x (2)

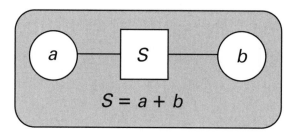

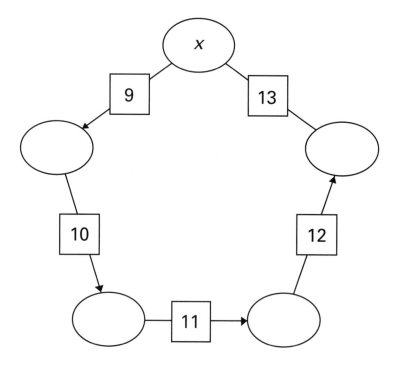

$$\underline{\hspace{4cm}}$$

$$x = \underline{\hspace{1.5cm}}$$

Solving linear equations: informal, preformal

Possible student work:

$2 + x + x = 13$

$\quad 2x = 11$

$\quad x = 5\tfrac{1}{2}$

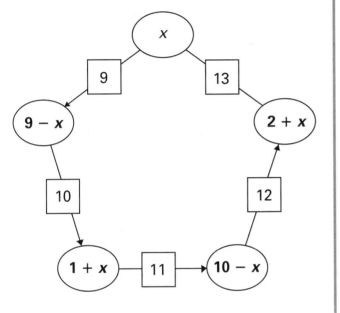

$$x = 5\tfrac{1}{2}$$

Difference in Temperature

All temperatures are in degrees Celsius.

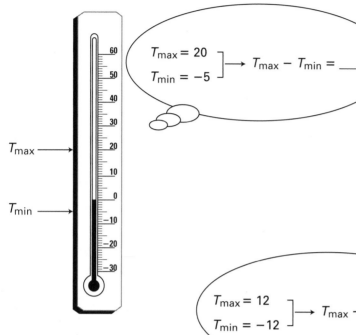

$T_{max} = 20$
$T_{min} = -5$ $\longrightarrow$ $T_{max} - T_{min} =$ _____

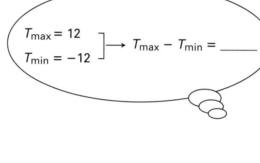

$T_{max} = 12$
$T_{min} = -12$ $\longrightarrow$ $T_{max} - T_{min} =$ _____

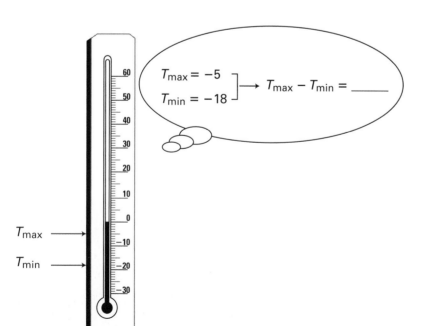

$T_{max} = -5$
$T_{min} = -18$ $\longrightarrow$ $T_{max} - T_{min} =$ _____

Computations with positive and negative numbers: informal

$T_{max} - T_{min} = 25$ (degrees)

$T_{max} - T_{min} = 24$ (degrees)

$T_{max} - T_{min} = 13$ (degrees)

Positive and Negative (1)

• Fill in the missing numbers.

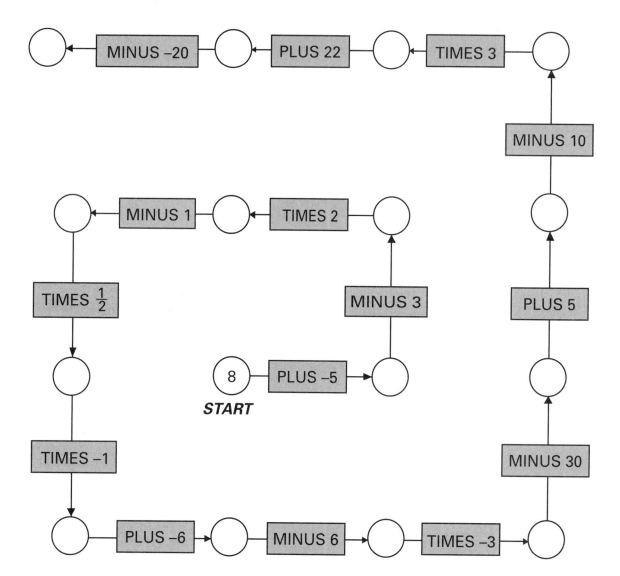

**Computations with positive and negative
numbers: preformal, formal**

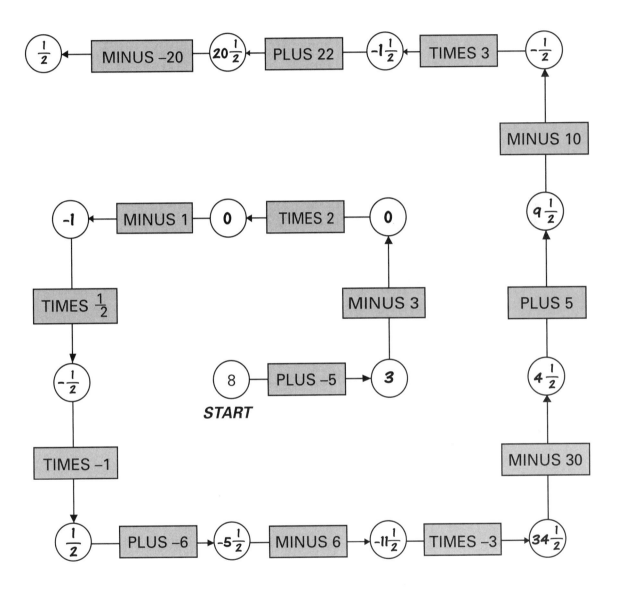

Positive and Negative (2)

• Fill in the missing numbers.

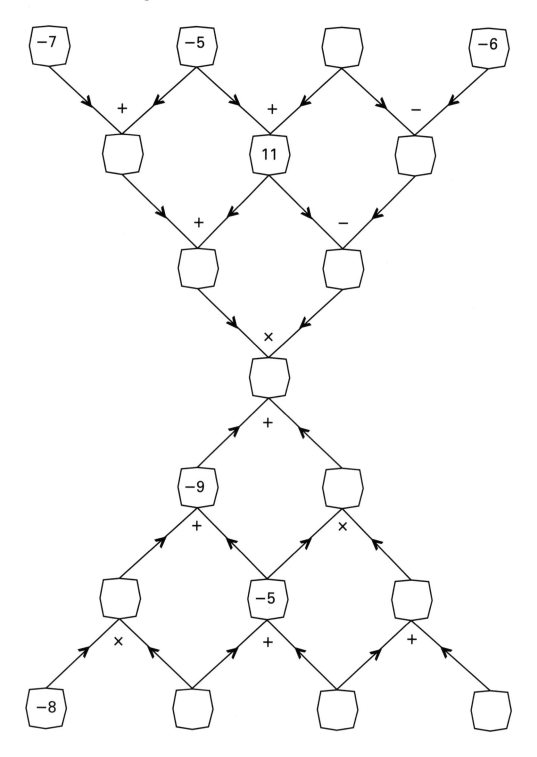

Computations with positive and negative
numbers: preformal, formal.

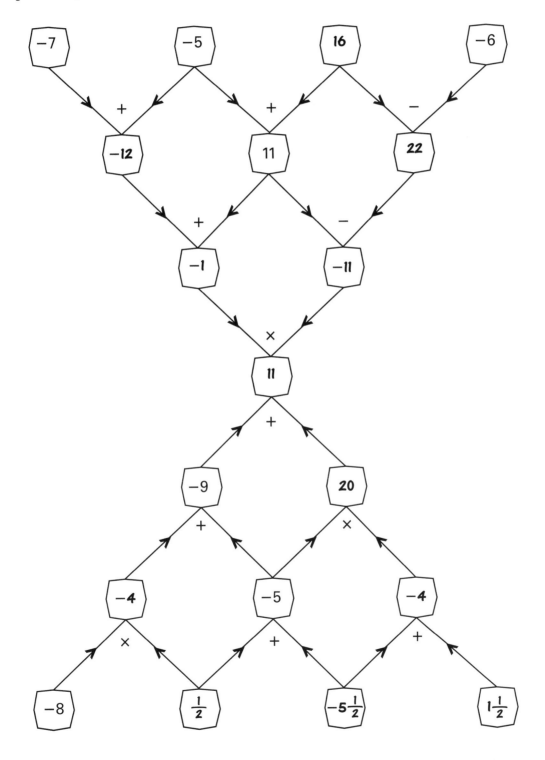

Positive and Negative (3)

$(25 - 28) - (32 - 40) =$ _____

$25 - (28 - 32) - 40 =$ _____

$25 - (28 - (32 - 40)) =$ _____

$25 - (28 - 32 - 40) =$ _____

$25 - 28 - (32 - 40) =$ _____

$25 - 28 - 32 - 40 =$ _____

Computations with positive and negative numbers: formal

$(25 - 28) - (32 - 40) =$ _____**5**_____

$25 - (28 - 32) - 40 =$ _____**−11**_____

$25 - (28 - (32 - 40)) =$ _____**−11**_____

$25 - (28 - 32 - 40) =$ _____**69**_____

$25 - 28 - (32 - 40) =$ _____**5**_____

$25 - 28 - 32 - 40 =$ _____**−75**_____

Positive and Negative (4)

A and **B** are integers.

$A + B = 5$

| $-6 < A < 6$ | ← | This means that **A** has a value between −6 and 6. |

- What can the value of **B** be? Of **A − B**? Of **B − A**?
- Fill in the chart.

A	B	A − B	B − A
−5			
−4			
−3			
−2			
−1			
0			
1			
2			
3			
4			
5			

Working with integers, presented as a variable:
formal

A	B	A − B	B − A
−5	10	-15	15
−4	9	-13	13
−3	8	-11	11
−2	7	-9	9
−1	6	-7	7
0	5	-5	5
1	4	-3	3
2	3	-1	1
3	2	1	-1
4	1	3	-3
5	0	5	-5

Diagonals of the Grid (1)

Look at the point (3, 2).

The sum of the *x*- and *y*- coordinates is 5, as is indicated by the flag.

A diagonal line is drawn through (3, 2).

- Check that the *x*-and *y*-coordinates of every grid point on this diagonal line have the same sum.

Between the grid points there are points that have fractions as coordinates.

- Indicate three such points on the diagonal line and check whether the sum of their coordinates is also 5.

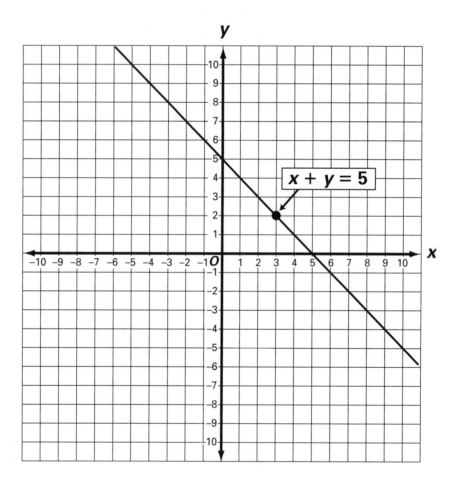

- Draw the diagonal line going through the points with coordinate sum −5. Label the line with *x* + *y* = −5.
- Draw a diagonal line parallel to the two diagonals already there so that it lies exactly in the middle between them. What label should you give this line?

Relating straight lines to equations, parallel lines

x	y	$x + y$
−5	10	5
−4	9	5
−3	8	5
−2	7	5
−1	6	5
0	5	5
1	4	5
2	3	5
3	2	5
4	1	5
5	0	5
6	−1	5
7	−2	5
8	−3	5
9	−4	5
10	−5	5

Sample grid points

x	y	$x + y$
$-1\frac{1}{2}$	$6\frac{1}{2}$	5
$1\frac{1}{2}$	$3\frac{1}{2}$	5
$-4\frac{1}{2}$	$9\frac{1}{2}$	5

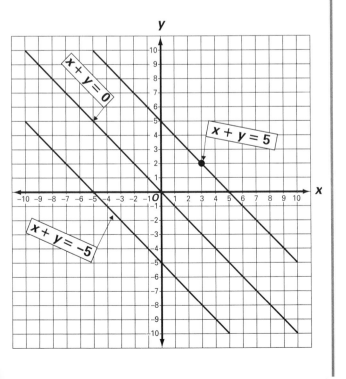

Diagonals of the Grid (2)

Look at the point (7, 2).

The difference of the x- and y-coordinates is 5.

- Draw the diagonal line through (7, 2) so that the x- and y- coordinates of every grid point on the diagonal line have the same difference and label it **x − y = 5.**

- Do the same, but now label the diagonal **y − x = 5.**

- Draw two other diagonals parallel to both lines and label each of them.

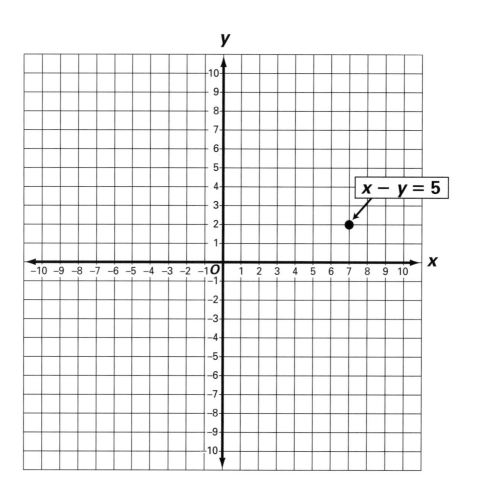

Relating straight lines to equations, parallel lines

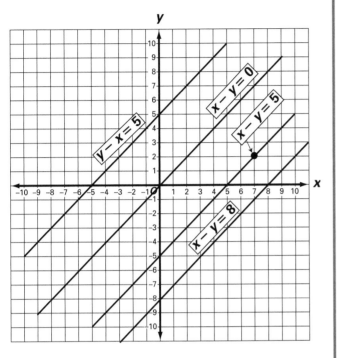

Other diagonals, parallel to these lines will vary.
Some sample labels are $x - y = 0$ and $x - y = 8$

Diagonals of the Grid (3)

- Draw the diagonals of the grid with labels $x + y = 7$ and $x - y = 3$.
  What are the coordinates of their point of intersection?

- Draw two diagonals going through the point $(-4, 2)$.
  How can you label these lines?

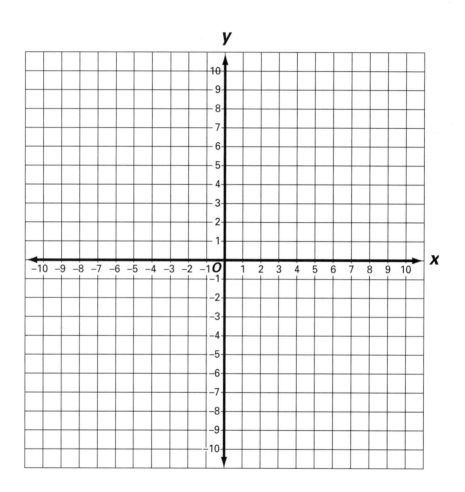

Intersection point of straight lines

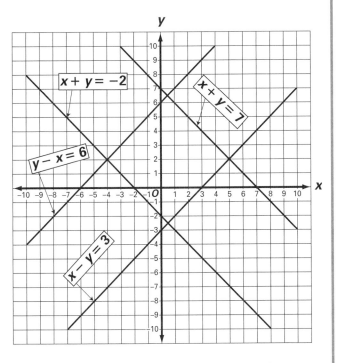

Intersection point: (5, 2) Note that reading the intersection point from the graph is a good strategy *if* the result is checked with the formula or equation:

$5 + 2 = 7$ and $5 - 2 = 3$.

Label of the lines through the point (−4, 2):
$x + y = -2$ $x - y = -6$

Multiplying on the Grid

Look at the arrow (**A**) in the grid. This figure has 7 vertices.
- Give the coordinates of these vertices.

If you multiply the *x*-coordinates of the vertices of **A** by –2,
you get a new arrow.
- Draw that new arrow.

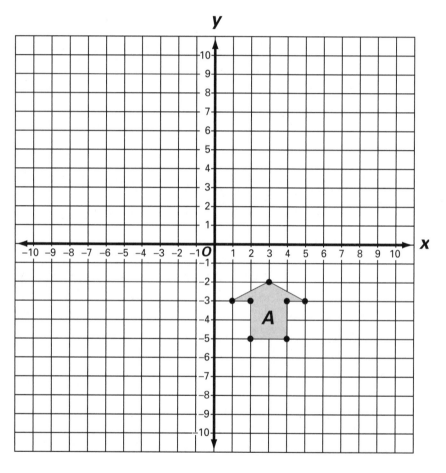

- Now multiply only the *y*-coordinates of **A** by –2 and draw
  the new arrow you get.

- Multiply both coordinates of **A** by –2 and draw the new
  arrow.

Operating with integers

Using coordinates

Transforming a shape

Coordinates of the vertices:

(3, –2); (5, –3); (4, –3); (4, –5); (2, –5); (2, –3); (1, –3)

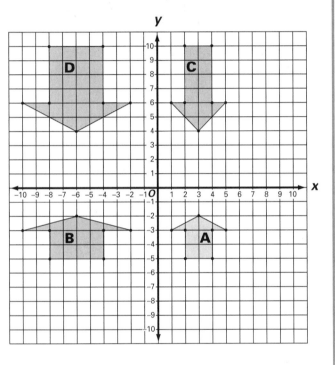

B; the *x*-coordinates of **A** are multiplied by 2
(–2, –3); (–6, –2); (–10, –3); (–8, –3); (–8, –5);
(–4, –5); (–4, –3)

C; the *y*-coordinates of **A** are multiplied by –2
(1, 6); (3, 4); (5, 6); (4, 6); (4, 10); (2, 10); (2, 6)

D; both coordinates of **A** are multiplied by –2.
(–2, 6); (–6, 4); (–10, 6); (–8, 6); (–8, 10); (–4, 10);
(–4, 6)

Colored Numbers (1)

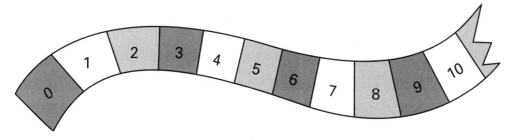

■ = red

☐ = blue

The number strip has a repeating pattern of
red-white-blue-red-white-blue, etc.

- What color is the cell of the number of your age?

- What color is the cell of number 67? Of 667?

- Explain why you can be sure that the color of the
  number 111 is red.

- What will the color of the number 1,111 be?

The numbers in the red cells can be described by
a formula:

$$red\ number = 3 \times n$$

- Explain this formula.

- Give a similar formula for the white numbers

- Give a similar formula for the blue numbers.

Finding patterns

Using formulas: informal, preformal

Multiples and divisors

- The color of the cell with the number of your age: Answers depend on the student's age.

  Note that the first cell is marked zero!

  Some examples:

age ten	color white
age eleven	color blue
age twelve	color red
age thirteen	color white
age fourteen	color blue

- Note that 0, 3, 6, 9, etc. are **red** numbers; these are multiples of three, or they are divisible by three. So 66 is a red number, and cell number 67 is **white**.

- Cell number 667 is also **white**. $666 \div 3 = 222$. Since 666 is a multiple of three, the next number is white.

- Cell number 111 is red. $111 \div 3 = 37$, so it is a multiple of three.

- Cell number 1,110 is red. Since 111 is a multiple of three, $10 \times 111 = 1,110$ is also a multiple of three. Cell 1,111 is **white**.

- *red number* $= 3 \times n$
  The first cell, $n = 0$, is red. $3 \times n$ are multiples of three, and these are all red.

- White numbers: *white number* $= 3 \times n + 1$ or *white number* $= 3n + 1$. Each white number succeeds a red number.

- Blue numbers: *blue number* $= 3 \times n + 2$ or *blue number* $= 3n + 2$. Each blue number comes two places after a red number or one place after a white number.

Colored Numbers (2)

This number strip has five colors.

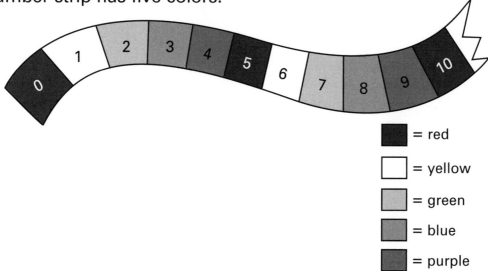

■ = red

☐ = yellow

▨ = green

▨ = blue

▨ = purple

- Write all the red numbers between 21 and 38.

- Write the first even yellow number after 100.

- How do you know that the number 99,999,999 is purple?

- Give a formula for the green numbers.

If you add a green and a blue number, the result will be red.
- Explain why.

Finding patterns and building linear formulas: preformal, formal

Multiples and divisors

Note that the first cell is marked zero!

- The red numbers between 21 and 38 are **25, 30**, and **35**.

Possible strategy:

red	0	5	10
yellow	1	6	11
green	2	7	
blue	3	8	
purple	4	9	

Each color is repeated after five numbers. Red: 0, 5, 10, 15, 20, 25, 30, 35, 40.

- The first even yellow number after 100 is **106**.

  Possible strategy:

  The yellow numbers are odd and even alternately ending with one or six: 1, 6, 11, 16, 21, 26, 31, 36.

- You can know number 99,999,999 is purple because purple numbers end with four or nine. Or you know that 1,000,000,000 is divisible by five, so it is a red number. The one preceding it is purple.

- A formula for any green number is

green number $= 2 + 5n$, where n starts with zero.

- Adding a green and a blue number results in a red number. Possible explanation:

  The first green number is 2; the first blue number is 3. $2 + 3 = 5$, which is a red number. All other colors are repeated after five numbers, and a multiple of 5 added to a multiple of 5 is still a multiple of five.

  Some students may use a more formal strategy,

  green number $= 2 + 5n$

  blue number $= 3 + 5m$

  green + *blue* $= 5 + 5n + 5m = 5(1 + n + m)$

  This number is a multiple of five, so it is a red number.

Name _____ Date_____ Class_____

Patterns of Gray Squares

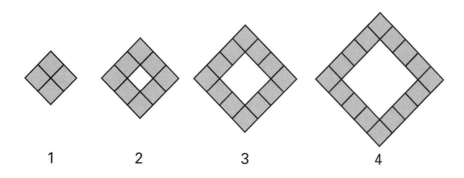

1   2   3   4

- How many gray squares will the pattern with number 5 have? The pattern with number 25?

- Give a formula for the number of gray squares (**R**) expressed in the number of the pattern (**n**).

R = _____

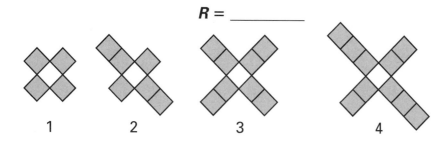

1   2   3   4

- Give a formula for the number of gray squares (**R**) expressed in the number of the pattern (**n**).

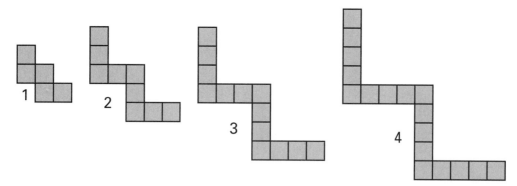

1   2   3   4

- Give a formula for the number of gray squares (**R**) expressed in the number of the pattern (**n**).

Finding patterns and building linear formulas: preformal, formal

First pattern:

- Pattern #5 has 20 squares. Pattern #25 has 100 squares.

  Look at regularities in the pattern or make a table and look at regularities in the table.

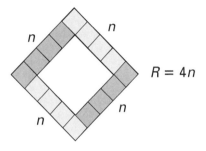

$R = 4n$

- $R = 4n$ or $R = 2(n + 1) + 2(n - 1)$

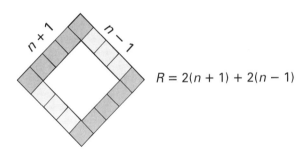

$R = 2(n + 1) + 2(n - 1)$

Second pattern:

- Each new pattern has two more squares.
  $R = 2 + 2n$

- Third pattern:
  $R = 1 + 4n$

Possible explanation:

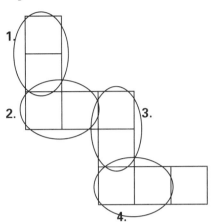

1.

2.   3.

4.

Patterns of Stars

1   2   3   4

- Give a formula for the number of stars (**S**) expressed in the number of the pattern (**n**).

S = _____

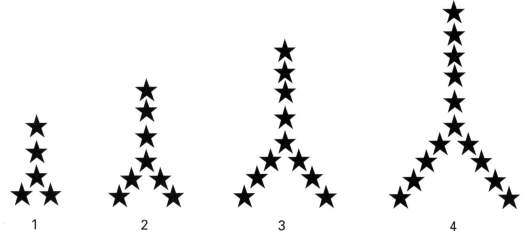

- Give a formula for the number of stars (**S**) expressed in the number of the pattern (**n**).

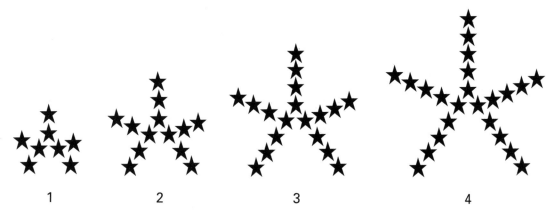

- Give a formula for the number of stars (**S**) expressed in the number of the pattern (**n**).

Finding patterns and building linear formulas: preformal, formal

- First pattern: (Note that this pattern is a *V*-pattern.)

  $S = 2n + 1$ or $n + (n + 1)$

- Second pattern:

  $S = 3n + 2$ or $2 + 3n$

- Third pattern:

  $S = 5n + 3$ or $S = 3 + 5n$

Arrow Strings (1)

- Fill in the missing numbers.

i

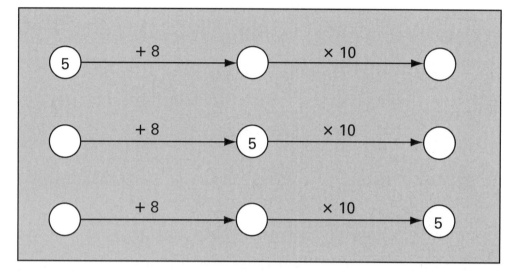

ii

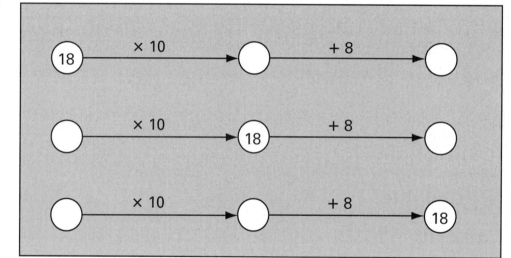

Look at these two formulas.

A = 10 × n + 8
B = 10 × (n + 8)

- Which of the two formulas corresponds to the arrow string?

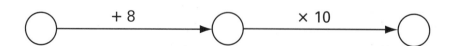

Mathematics in Context

Chains of operations

Anticipating the use of distributive property

i

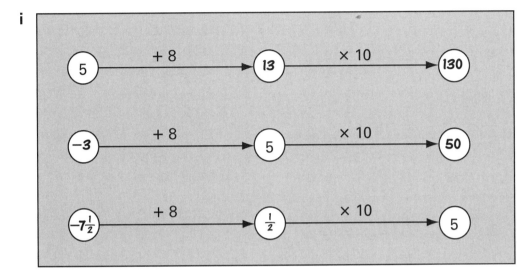

ii

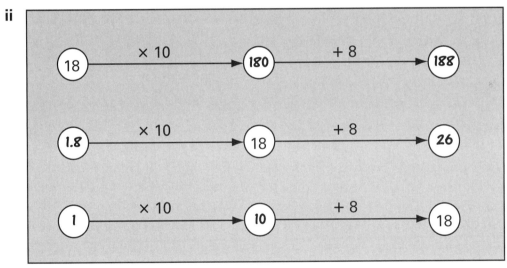

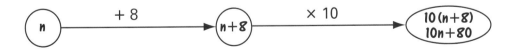

formula **B** = 10 × (**n** + 8) corresponds to the arrow string

Arrow Strings (2)

• Fill in the missing numbers.

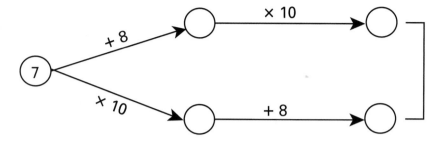

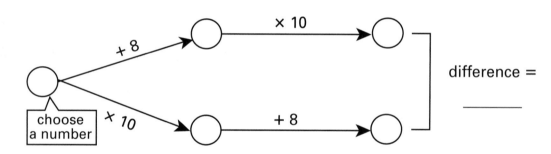

• Fill in the missing expressions.

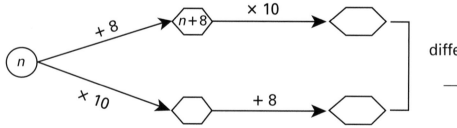

Chains of operations

Anticipating the use of distributive property

Operations with expressions

difference is $150 - 78 = 72$

difference is $10 - (-62) = 72$

difference is $130 - 58 = 72$

missing expressions: $(n + 8) \times 10$; $10n$ and $10n + 8$

Difference:

$$
\begin{array}{r}
10n + 80 \\
- \quad 10n + 8 \\
\hline
72
\end{array}
$$

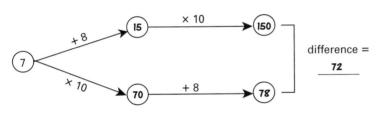

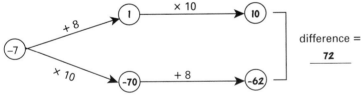

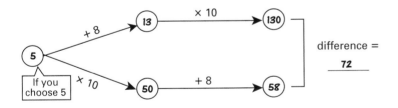

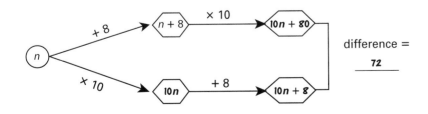

Arrow Strings (3)

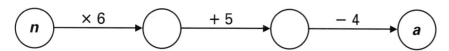

- Give a formula that corresponds to the first arrow string.

$$a = _____$$

You can change the order of the three "operators" ×6, +5, −4.
This leads to five new arrow strings.

- Give a formula to each of these five arrow strings.

$b = $ _____

$c = $ _____

$d = $ _____

$e = $ _____

$f = $ _____

Chains of operations

Anticipating the use of distributive property

Operations with expressions

- $a = 6n + 5 - 4 = 6n + 1$
- The other arrow strings depend on the operators students used. The letters b, c, d, e, and f are interchangeable.

$$n \xrightarrow{\times 6} 6n \xrightarrow{-4} 6n - 4 \xrightarrow{+5} b$$
$$b = 6n - 4 + 5 = 6n + 1$$

$$n \xrightarrow{+5} n + 5 \xrightarrow{\times 6} 6(n + 5) \xrightarrow{-4} c$$
$$c = 6(n + 5) - 4 = 6n + 26$$

$$n \xrightarrow{+5} n + 5 \xrightarrow{-4} n + 1 \xrightarrow{\times 6} d$$
$$d = 6(n + 1) = 6n + 6$$

$$n \xrightarrow{-4} n - 4 \xrightarrow{\times 6} 6(n - 4) \xrightarrow{+5} e$$
$$e = 6(n - 4) + 5 = 6n - 19$$

$$n \xrightarrow{-4} n - 4 \xrightarrow{+5} n + 1 \xrightarrow{\times 6} f$$
$$f = 6(n + 1) = 6n + 6$$

Note that only four equations are different. Discuss with your class why this is the case. Discuss the effects of the order of operations.

Arrow Strings (4)

• Fill in the missing expressions.

Operations with expressions: preformal

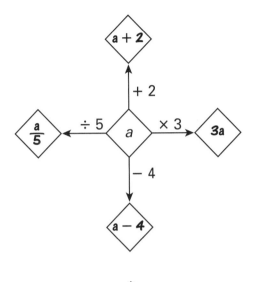

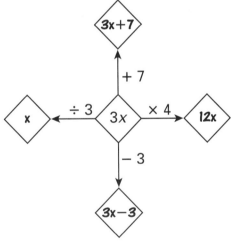

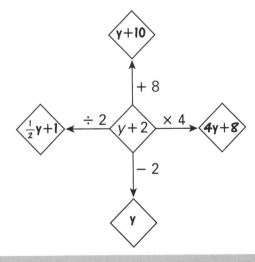

Arrow Strings (5)

• Fill in the missing expressions.

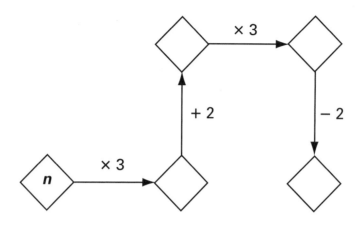

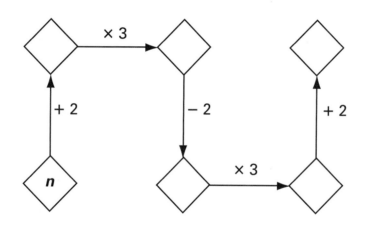

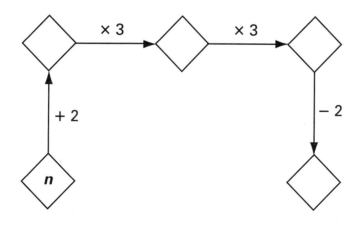

Chains of operations

Operations with expressions

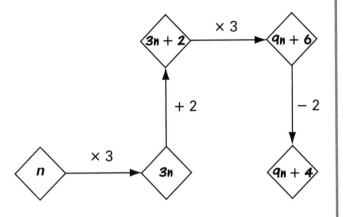

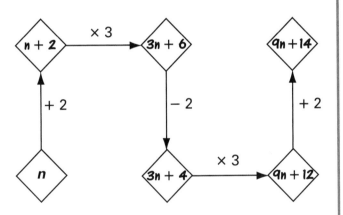

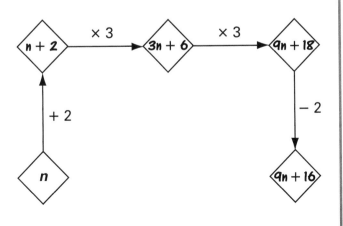

Name _____ Date _____ Class_____

Operating with Number Strips (1)

• Fill in the missing numbers and expressions.

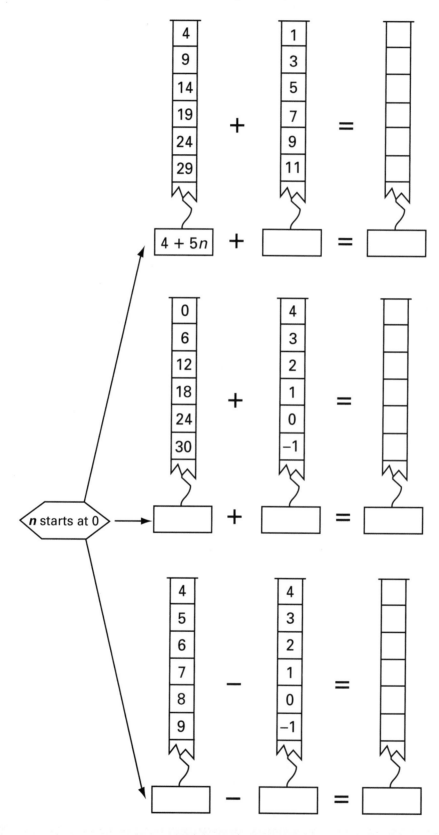

n starts at 0

© Encyclopædia Britannica, Inc. This page may be reproduced for classroom use.

Mathematics in Context

Finding patterns in numbers

Building expressions

Operations with expressions

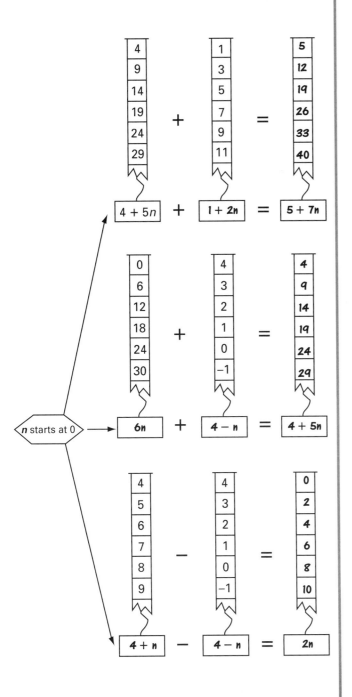

Operating with Number Strips (2)

• Fill in the missing numbers and expressions. In each case *n* starts at 0.

$4 \times \quad \begin{array}{|c|}\hline 2 \\\hline 5 \\\hline 8 \\\hline 11 \\\hline 14 \\\hline 17 \\\hline 20 \\\hline\end{array} \quad = \quad \begin{array}{|c|}\hline 8 \\\hline \\\hline \\\hline \\\hline \\\hline \\\hline\end{array} \qquad \frac{1}{3} \times \quad \begin{array}{|c|}\hline 3 \\\hline 9 \\\hline 15 \\\hline 21 \\\hline 27 \\\hline 33 \\\hline 39 \\\hline\end{array} \quad = \quad \begin{array}{|c|}\hline \\\hline \\\hline \\\hline \\\hline \\\hline \\\hline\end{array}$

$4 \times \boxed{} = \boxed{} \qquad \frac{1}{3} \times \boxed{} = \boxed{}$

$8 \times \quad \begin{array}{|c|}\hline 2 \\\hline 7 \\\hline 12 \\\hline 17 \\\hline 22 \\\hline 27 \\\hline 32 \\\hline\end{array} \quad + \quad 3 \times \quad \begin{array}{|c|}\hline 10 \\\hline 5 \\\hline 0 \\\hline -5 \\\hline -10 \\\hline -20 \\\hline -25 \\\hline\end{array} \quad = \quad \begin{array}{|c|}\hline \\\hline \\\hline \\\hline \\\hline \\\hline \\\hline\end{array}$

$8 \times \boxed{} + 3 \times \boxed{} = \boxed{}$

Finding patterns in numbers
Building expressions
Operations with expressions

$$4 \times \begin{array}{|c|} \hline 2 \\ \hline 5 \\ \hline 8 \\ \hline 11 \\ \hline 14 \\ \hline 17 \\ \hline 20 \\ \hline \end{array} = \begin{array}{|c|} \hline 8 \\ \hline 20 \\ \hline 32 \\ \hline 44 \\ \hline 56 \\ \hline 68 \\ \hline 80 \\ \hline \end{array} \qquad \frac{1}{3} \times \begin{array}{|c|} \hline 3 \\ \hline 9 \\ \hline 15 \\ \hline 21 \\ \hline 27 \\ \hline 33 \\ \hline 39 \\ \hline \end{array} = \begin{array}{|c|} \hline 1 \\ \hline 3 \\ \hline 5 \\ \hline 7 \\ \hline 9 \\ \hline 11 \\ \hline 13 \\ \hline \end{array}$$

$$4 \times \boxed{2 + 3n} = \boxed{8 + 12n} \qquad \frac{1}{3} \times \boxed{3 + 6n} = \boxed{1 + 2n}$$

$$8 \times \begin{array}{|c|} \hline 2 \\ \hline 7 \\ \hline 12 \\ \hline 17 \\ \hline 22 \\ \hline 27 \\ \hline 32 \\ \hline \end{array} + 3 \times \begin{array}{|c|} \hline 10 \\ \hline 5 \\ \hline 0 \\ \hline -5 \\ \hline -10 \\ \hline -15 \\ \hline -20 \\ \hline \end{array} = \begin{array}{|c|} \hline 46 \\ \hline 71 \\ \hline 96 \\ \hline 121 \\ \hline 146 \\ \hline 171 \\ \hline 196 \\ \hline \end{array}$$

$$8 \times \boxed{2 + 5n} + 3 \times \boxed{10 - 5n} = \boxed{46 + 25n}$$

Strips and Charts (1)

$2 + 3n$

$5 + 2m$ **+**

2	5	8	11	14	17	20	23

5	7	10	13	16	19	22	26	28
7	9	12	15	18	21	24	27	30
9	11	14	17	20	23	26	29	32
11	13	16	19	22	25	28	31	34
13	15	18	21	24	27	30	33	36
15	17	20	23	26	29	32	35	38
17	19	22	25	28	31	34	37	40
19	21	24	27	30	33	36	39	42

$7 + 2m + 3n$

- Find the number in the chart that corresponds to $m = 3$ and $n = 2$.

- Find the number that corresponds to $m = 3$ and $n = 5$.

- Which horizontal row in the chart does $m = 4$ corresponds to?

- Which vertical column does $n = 5$ correspond to?

- Which numbers in the chart correspond to $m = n$?

- Make a number strip for the numbers that correspond to $m = n$ with a corresponding expression.

Adding expressions with two variables: preformal

Substitution

- The number that corresponds to $m = 3$ and $n = 2$ is $11 + 8 = 19$.

- The number that corresponds to $m = 3$ and $n = 5$ is $11 + 17 = 28$.

- The horizontal row 15 18 21 24 27 30 33 36 corresponds to $m = 4$.

- The vertical column 22 24 26 28 30 32 34 36 corresponds to $n = 5$.

- The diagonal 7 12 17 22 27 32 37 42 corresponds to $m = n$.

  Note that students may replace n by m in the expression, which results in

  $7 + 2m + 3m = 7 + 5m$.

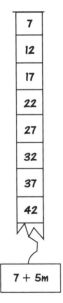

Strips and Charts (2)

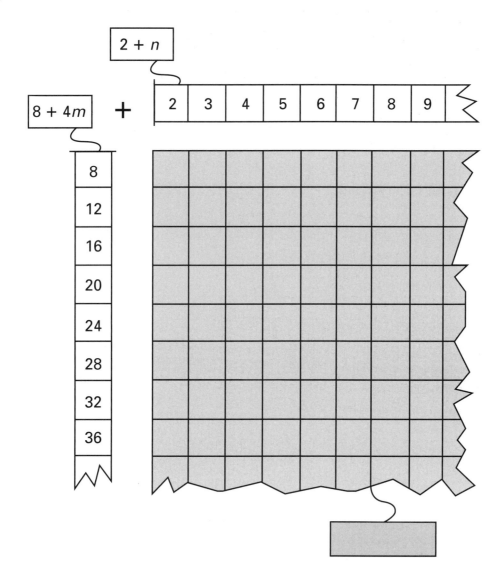

- Fill in the chart. What expression fits the chart?

- What strip fits **m = 3**? What is the corresponding expression?

- Answer the same questions for **n = 0**.

- For **m = n**.

- For **m = n + 1**.

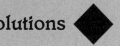
Adding expressions with two variables: preformal Substitution

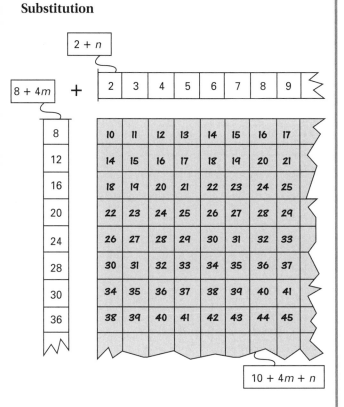

- The strip that fits with $m = 3$ is 22 23 24 25 26 27 28 29. The corresponding expression is $8 + 4 \times 3 + 2 + n = 22 + n$.

- The strip that fits with $n = 0$ is 10 14 18 22 26 30 34 38. The corresponding expression is $2 + 0 + 8 + 4m = 10 + 4m$.

- The strip that fits with $m = n$ is 10 15 20 25 30 35 40 45. The corresponding expression is $8 + 4m + 2 + m = 10 + 5m$.

- The strip that fits with $m = n + 1$ is 14 19 24 29 34 39 44. The corresponding expression is $8 + 4(n + 1) + 2 + n = 8 + 4n + 4 + 2 + n = 14 + 5$

Strips and Charts (3)

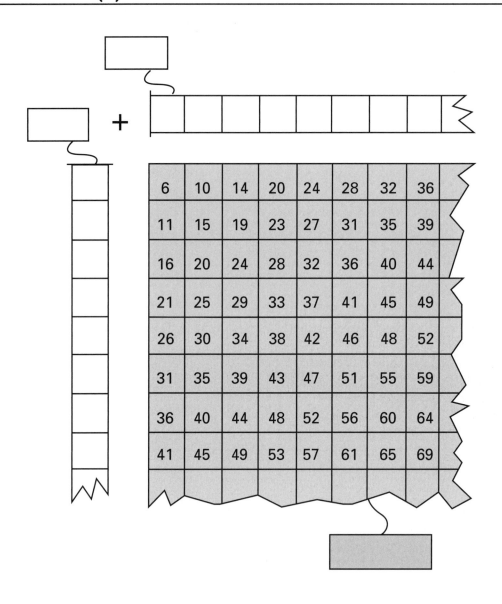

- What expression fits the chart?

- What strips can be used to make the chart?

Adding expressions with two variables: preformal

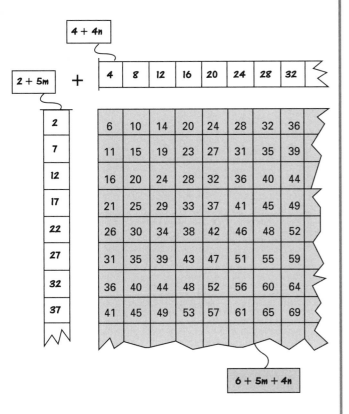

This is one possibility. Discuss with students what other possibilities there are for the expressions. For example: is $3 + 5m$ and $3 + 4n$ also possible?

Operating with Expressions (1)

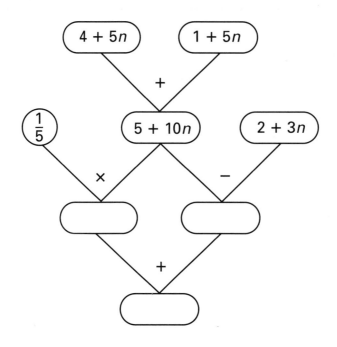

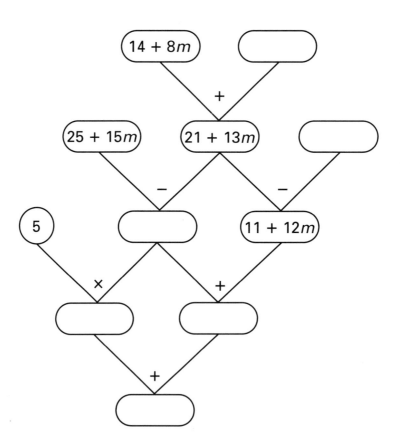

Adding and subtracting expressions and multiplying by a constant

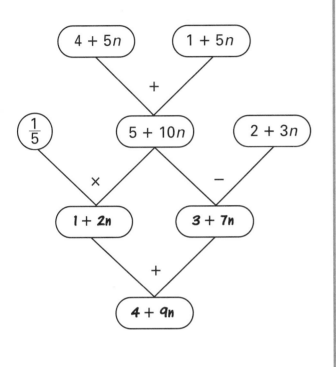

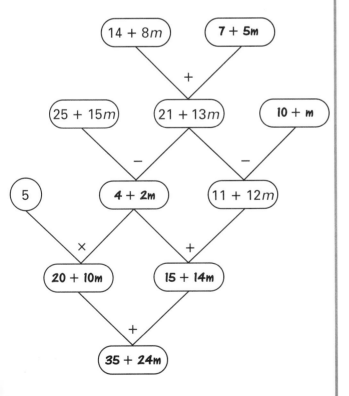

Operating with Expressions (2)

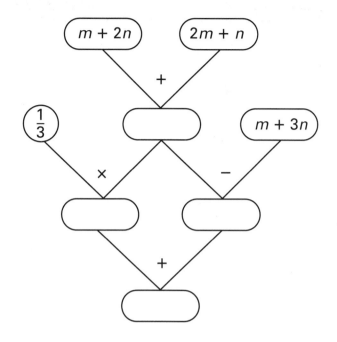

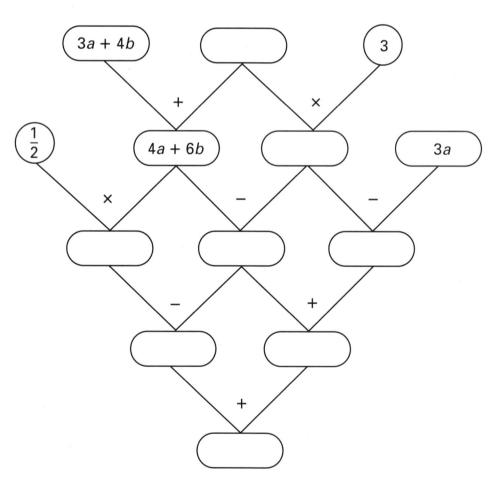

Operating with Expressions (2)

**Adding and subtracting expressions and
multiplying by a constant**

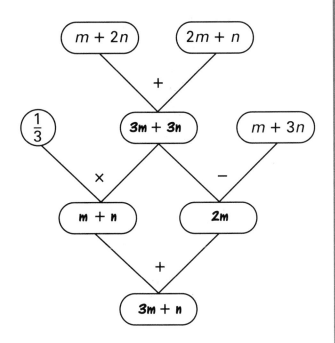

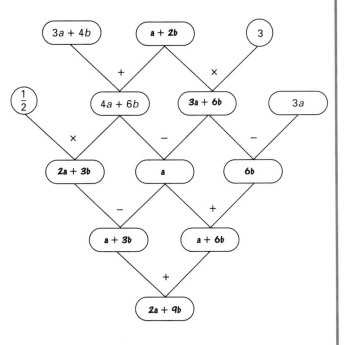

Algebra in Balance (1)

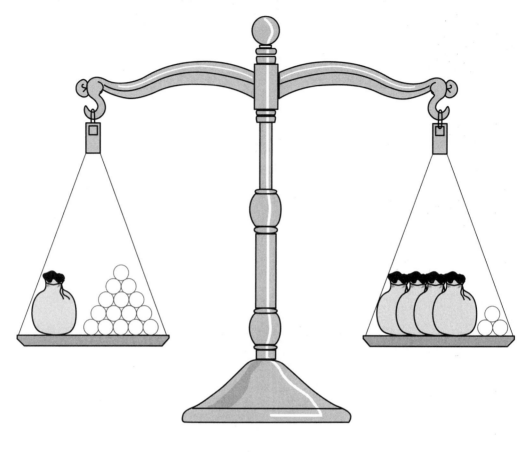

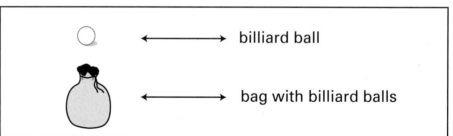

billiard ball

bag with billiard balls

Each bag contains the same number of billiard balls.
- Calculate this number. Ignore the weight of the bags.

Informal solving of a simple linear equation using the "balance method"

1 bag	4 bags	take away 1 bag from each side
15 balls	3 balls	
15 balls	3 bags	take away 3 balls from each side
	3 balls	
12 balls	3 bags	Each bag contains 4 balls.
4 + 4 + 4 balls	3 bags	

Algebra in Balance (2)

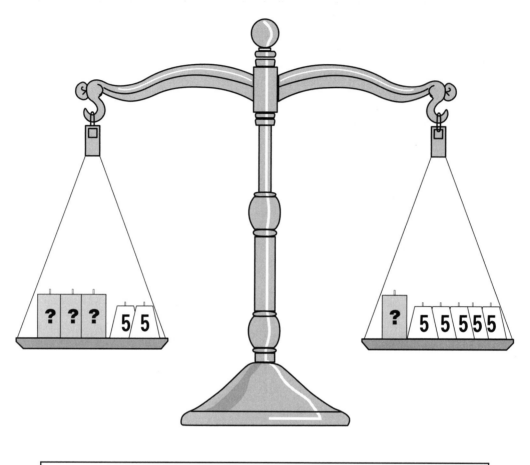

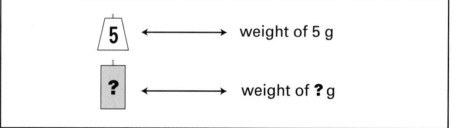

5 ←————→	weight of 5 g
? ←————→	weight of **?** g

The weights are perfectly in balance.

• Calculate the weight marked by **?**.

Informal solving of a simple linear equation using the "balance method"

2 weights 3 ?	5 weights 1 ?
3 ?	3 weights 1 ?
2 ?	3 weights

take away 2 weights of 5 kg from each side

take away 1 weight of ? from each side

Two weights with a question mark are in balance with 3 weights of 5 kg or 15 kg.

The weights with the question marks are $7\frac{1}{2}$ kg each.

Note that some students may use a more formal method, making (word) variables.

Calendar Problems (1)

On a calendar for June 2004, a horizontal block of three consecutive dates is chosen. The sum of the three dates is 48 (15 + 16 + 17 = 48).

Sun	Mon	Tue	Wed	Thu	Fri	Sat
		1	2	3	4	5
6	7	8	9	10	11	12
13	14	15	16	17	18	19
20	21	22	23	24	25	26
27	28	29	30			

Another set of consecutive dates is chosen. The sum of the dates is 72.
- Which three dates are chosen?

Take another month. On the calendar for that month, three consecutive dates are chosen. Their sum is 39.
- Which dates are chosen?

Go back to the calendar for June 2004. On the calendar, a *vertical* block of three dates is chosen. Their sum is 54.
- Which dates are chosen?

- Is there a vertical block of *four* dates with sum 54? If so, which one?

The third Tuesday in May 2004 was the 15th. This is the smallest possible number that the third Tuesday in any month can have.
- Explain why.

- What is the largest possible number the third Tuesday of a month can have? Show your work.

Solving word problems, linear equations: informal

- Note that since 72 > 48, the set of dates must be later in the month. Students may use trial and error to find the dates 23, 24, and 25. They may also reason that 72 ÷ 3 = 24, so 24 is in the middle.

- Students may use trial and error to find the dates 12, 13, and 14. They may also reason that 39 ÷ 3 = 13, so 13 is in the middle.

- Students may use trial and error to find the dates 11, 18, and 25. They may also reason that 54 ÷ 3 = 18, so 18 is in the middle and the other numbers are seven before and after 18.

- There is 1 possibility for a vertical set of four with a sum of 54. The dates are 3, 10, 17, and 24.

- The first Tuesday may be the first day of the month; there is no earlier possible date. Then the second Tuesday is date 8; the third Tuesday is 15.

- The first Tuesday may be on the 7th, there is no later possible date. Then the second Tuesday is date 14; the third Tuesday is 21.

Name _____ **Date**_____ **Class**_____

Calendar Problems (2)

On the calendar of a month with 30 days, a horizontal block of *five* consecutive dates is chosen. The sum of the five numbers is 105.

Sun	Mon	Tue	Wed	Thu	Fri	Sat
			x			

• Use x for the middle number and make expressions for the other four numbers.

• Calculate the value of x. (Hint: Use an equation.)

• Look at the calendar. Which day is the first of that month?

On the calendar for another month, a *vertical* block of *four* dates is chosen. The sum of the four numbers is 54.

• Use x for the smallest number and make expressions for the other three numbers.

• Calculate the value of x.

Solving word problems, linear equations: preformal

- The four expressions are $x - 2$; $x - 1$; $x + 1$; $x + 2$.

- Note that students still working at an informal level may try to find the answer by trial and error. Encourage them to use an equation.

  The equation to be solved is $x - 2 + x - 1 + x + x + 1 + x + 2 = 105$

  $5x = 105$

  $x = 21$

  The five consecutive numbers are 19, 20, 21, 22, and 23.

  Have students check the answer by adding the numbers.

- The first day is a Thursday. Subtracting three times 7 from 21 results in 0, so the day before the month started was a Wednesday.

  The three expressions are $x + 7$; $x + 14$, and $x + 21$.

  The equation to be solved is $x + x + 7 + x + 14 + x + 21 = 54$.

  $4x + 42 = 54$

  $4x = 12$

  $x = 3$

Solving Equations (1)

$v + 14 + v = 25 + v + 14 \longrightarrow v = $ _____

$w + 20 + w = 25 + w + 30 \longrightarrow w = $ _____

$x + 28 + x = 14 + x + 14 \longrightarrow x = $ _____

$y + y + 10 + y = 60 + y \longrightarrow y = $ _____

$z + 60 + z + z = 10 + z \longrightarrow z = $ _____

Solving linear equations using integers: formal

- $v = 25$
  Possible strategies:

  - $v + 14 + v = 25 + v + 14$ Subtract $v + 14$ from both sides of the equation: $v = 25$.

  - $2v + 14 = v + 39$
    Using the method "difference is zero":

    $$\begin{array}{r} 2v + 14 \\ - \quad v + 39 \\ \hline v - 25 = 0 \\ v = 25 \end{array}$$

    Only two strategies are shown here. You may want to discuss different solution strategies with your students.

- $w = 35$
  Possible strategies:

  - $w + 20 + w = 25 + w + 30$ Subtract $w + 20$ from both sides.

    $w = 5 + 30$
    $w = 35$

- $x = 0$
  Possible strategies:

  - $x + 28 + x = x + 28$ Subtract $x + 28$ from both sides of the equation: $x = 0$.

  - $2x + 28 = x + 28$ Subtract 28 from both sides.

  - $2x = x$ This can only be true if $x = 0$.

- $y = 25$
  Possible strategies:

  - $y + y + 10 + y = 60 + y$ Subtract $y + 10$ from both sides.

    $y + y = 50$
    $y = 25$

  - $3y + 10 = 60 + y$ Using the "difference is zero" method.

    $$\begin{array}{r} 3y + 10 \\ - \quad y + 60 \\ \hline 2y - 50 = 0 \\ 2y = 50 \\ y = 25 \end{array}$$

- $z = -25$
  Possible strategies:

  - $z + 60 + z + z = 10 + z$ Subtract $10 + z$ from both sides.

    $z + z + 50 = 0$
    $z + z = -50$
    $z = -25$

  - $3z + 60 = 10 + z$ Using the "difference is zero" method.

    $$\begin{array}{r} 3z + 60 \\ - \quad z + 10 \\ \hline 2z + 50 = 0 \\ 2z = -50 \\ z = -25 \end{array}$$

Solving Equations (2)

$24a + 12 = 20a + 52$

$\downarrow$

$a = $ _____

$204a + 121 = 200a + 521$

$\downarrow$

$a = $ _____

$2004a + 1218 = 2000a + 5218$

$\downarrow$

$a = $ _____

$35b - 11 = 30b - 6$

$\downarrow$

$b = $ _____

$350b - 110 = 300b - 60$

$\downarrow$

$b = $ _____

$3500b - 1100 = 3000b - 600$

$\downarrow$

$b = $ _____

Solving linear equations: formal

$a = 10$ $b = 1$
$a = 100$ $b = 1$
$a = 1000$ $b = 1$

Discuss different strategies.
Possible student answers:
Using the method "difference is zero":

$$
\begin{array}{r}
24a + 12 \\
20a + 52 \\
\hline
4a - 40 = 0 \\
4a = 40 \\
a = 10
\end{array}
$$

- Note the relationship between the first, second, and third equation and use it to solve these equations.

- Using the "add or subtract the same number" or "balance" method:

$$
\begin{array}{rlrl}
204a + 121 & = & 200a + 521 \\
- 200a & & - 200a \\
\hline
4a + 121 & = & 521 \\
- \quad\quad 121 & & - 121 \\
\hline
4a & = & 400 \\
a & = & 100
\end{array}
$$

$$
\begin{array}{rlrl}
2004a + 1218 & = & 2000a + 5218 \\
- 2000a & & - 2000a \\
\hline
4a + 1218 & = & 5218 \\
- \quad\quad 1218 & & - 1218 \\
\hline
4a & = & 4000 \\
a & = & 1000
\end{array}
$$

Second set of equations:

- Note the relationship between the first, second, and third equation and use it to solve these equations.

$$
\begin{array}{r}
35b - 11 \\
30b - 6 \\
\hline
5b - 5 = 0 \\
5b = 5 \\
b = 1
\end{array}
$$

$$
\begin{array}{r}
350b - 110 \\
300b - 60 \\
\hline
50b - 50 = 0 \\
50b = 50 \\
b = 1
\end{array}
$$

$$
\begin{array}{rlrl}
3500b - 1100 & = & 3000b - 600 \\
- 3000b & & - 3000b \\
\hline
500b - 1100 & = & -600 \\
+ 1100 & & + 1100 \\
\hline
500b & = & 500 \\
b & = & 1
\end{array}
$$

Solving Equations (3)

On this page, you see eight equations. They can be divided
in two groups in such a way that all equations in each group
have the same solution. Try to decide if two equations
belong to the same group without solving the equations!

- Choose one equation and connect it with all the equations
  that belong to the same group.
- Check to see whether the remaining equations also belong
  to the same group.

$4a + 17 = 3a + 22$

$4a + 17 = 3a + 21$

$4a + 15 = 3a + 20$

$3a + 17 = 2a + 22$

$8a + 34 = 6a + 42$

$40a + 170 = 30a + 220$

$4a + 17 = 3(a + 7)$

$2a + 7\frac{1}{2} = 1\frac{1}{2}a + 10$

Comparing linear equations, equivalence: formal

Choices of students for the equation to start with will differ. Students could, for example, reason that $4a + 17 = 3a + 21$ and $8a + 34 = 6a + 42$ belong to the same group because the second equation is similar to the first—all terms are multiplied by two.

The two groups with the same solution are:

$$4a + 17 = 3a + 21 \qquad \times 2$$
$$8a + 34 = 6a + 42 \qquad \times 10$$

$$4a + 17 = 3(a + 7)$$
$$\text{since } 3(a + 7) = 3a + 21$$

$$\times 10 \left(
\begin{array}{l}
4a + 17 = 3a + 22 \quad {-2} \\
4a + 15 = 3a + 20 \\
2a + 7\tfrac{1}{2} = 1\tfrac{1}{2}a + 10 \quad {\div 2} \\
3a + 17 = 2a + 22 \\
40a + 170 = 30a + 220
\end{array}
\right) - a$$

(Dis)covering (1)

Example:

$$\frac{1}{2 + 5x} = \frac{1}{12} \longrightarrow x = ?$$

cover $2 + 5x$

$$\frac{1}{} = \frac{1}{12}$$

$$\downarrow$$

$$12$$

$$2 + 5x = 12$$

$$5x = 10$$

$$\boxed{x = 2}$$

Use the "cover" method to solve.

$$\frac{1}{8 - x} = \frac{1}{3}$$

$$\frac{1}{3 - x} = \frac{1}{8}$$

$$\frac{5}{\frac{1}{2}x + 1} = \frac{5}{6}$$

$$\frac{6}{2x + 1} = \frac{3}{4}$$

$$\frac{100}{3x + 4} = 10$$

$$\frac{1000}{31x + 69} = 10$$

Solving linear equations using the "cover" method: formal

$$\frac{1}{8 - x} = \frac{1}{3}$$
$$8 - x = 3$$
$$x = 5$$

$$\frac{1}{3 - x} = \frac{1}{8}$$
$$3 - x = 8$$
$$x = -5$$

$$\frac{5}{\frac{1}{2}x + 1} = \frac{5}{6}$$
$$\frac{1}{2}x + 1 = 6$$
$$\frac{1}{2}x = 5$$
$$x = 10$$

$$\frac{6}{2x + 1} = \frac{3}{4}$$
$$\frac{6}{8} = \frac{3}{4}, \text{ so } 2x + 1 = 8$$
$$2x = 7$$
$$x = 3\tfrac{1}{2}$$

$$\frac{100}{3x + 4} = 10$$
$$\frac{100}{10} = 10, \text{ so } 3x + 4 = 10$$
$$3x = 6$$
$$x = 2$$

$$\frac{1,000}{31x + 69} = 10$$
$$\frac{1,000}{100} = 10, \text{ so } 31x + 69 = 100$$
$$31x = 31$$
$$x = 1$$

(Dis)covering (2)

Solve for **x**.

$$\sqrt{x} = 5$$

$$4\sqrt{10 - x} = 12$$

$$\sqrt{4 + 3x} = 5$$

$$\sqrt{10 + \sqrt{x}} = 4$$

$$2 + \sqrt{3x} = 5$$

$$\sqrt{30 + \sqrt{30 + x}} = 6$$

$$\sqrt{10 + x} = 3$$

$$\sqrt{20 + \sqrt{20 + \sqrt{x}}} = 5$$

Solving linear equations using the "cover" method: formal

$\sqrt{x} = 5$
$\quad x = 25$

$\sqrt{4 + 3x} = 5$
$\quad 4 + 3x = 25$
$\qquad 3x = 21$
$\qquad\ x = 7$

$2 + \sqrt{3x} = 5$
$2 + \sqrt{3x} - 2 = 5 - 2$ $\quad$ First subtract 2 from both sides.
$\qquad \sqrt{3x} = 3$
$\qquad\ 3x = 9$
$\qquad\ \ x = 3$

$\sqrt{10 + x} = 3$
$\quad 10 + x = 9$
$\qquad\ x = -1$

$4\sqrt{10 - x} = 12$
$(4\sqrt{10 - x}) \div 4 = 12 \div 4$ $\quad$ First divide both sides by 4.
$\qquad \sqrt{10 - x} = 3$
$\qquad 10 - x = 9$
$\qquad\qquad x = 1$

$\sqrt{10 + \sqrt{x}} = 4$
$(\sqrt{10 + \sqrt{x}})^2 = 4^2$ $\quad$ First square both sides to get rid of
$\qquad\qquad\qquad\qquad$ the first square root.
$\qquad 10 + \sqrt{x} = 16$
$10 + \sqrt{x} - 10 = 16 - 10$ $\quad$ Then subtract 10 from both sides.
$\qquad\qquad \sqrt{x} = 6$
$\qquad\qquad\ x = 36$

$\sqrt{30 + \sqrt{30 + x}} = 6$
$(\sqrt{30 + \sqrt{30 + x}})^2 = 6^2$ $\quad$ First square both sides to get rid of
$\qquad\qquad\qquad\qquad\qquad$ the first square root.
$\qquad 30 + \sqrt{30 + x} = 36$
$30 + \sqrt{30 + x} - 30 = 36 - 30$ $\quad$ Then subtract 30 from both sides.
$\qquad\qquad \sqrt{30 + x} = 6$
$\qquad\qquad\ 30 + x = 36$
$\qquad\qquad\qquad\ x = 6$

$\sqrt{20 + \sqrt{20 + \sqrt{x}}} = 5$
$(\sqrt{20 + \sqrt{20 + \sqrt{x}}})^2 = 5^2$ $\quad$ First square both sides to get rid of
$\qquad\qquad\qquad\qquad\qquad\qquad$ the first square root.
$\qquad 20 + \sqrt{20 + \sqrt{x}} = 25$
$20 + \sqrt{20 + \sqrt{x}} - 20 = 25 - 20$ $\quad$ Then subtract 20 from both sides.
$\qquad\qquad \sqrt{20 + \sqrt{x}} = 5$ $\quad$ Then square both sides again.
$\qquad\qquad\ 20 + \sqrt{x} = 25$
$20 + \sqrt{x} - 20 = 25 - 20$ $\quad$ Then subtract 20 from both sides.
$\qquad\qquad\qquad \sqrt{x} = 5$
$\qquad\qquad\qquad\ x = 25$

Problems of Diophantos (1)

Diophantos was a Greek mathematician who lived in Alexandria in the third century. He wrote a book called *Arithmetica* that has 130 problems about numbers, which are solved by using equations. He may have been the first one who used a symbol for unknown numbers, and, therefore, he is sometimes called the "father of algebra."

Diophantos's epitaph:

> Here lies Diophantos, a math wonder to behold,
> With the use of algebra, the stones tell how old:
> One-sixth of his life, he spent as a child,
> One-twelfth more, and his beard grew wild,
> Adding one-seventh more to his life,
> He decided to marry, and so took a wife,
> Five years passed, and he had a bouncing boy,
> Life seemed perfect, filled with love and joy.
> But alas, the dear son of master and sage,
> After reaching half of his father's full age,
> Died and was laid in a cold, chilly grave,
> While his father, trying his best to be brave,
> Busied himself in the science of numbers,
> Then in four years, enjoyed Eternal Slumbers.

• Try to find out to what age Diophantos lived.
  (Hint: Suppose this age is *a*; use *a* to write an equation.)

Historic word problems

Solving a (complicated) linear equation using fractions

Diophantos was 84 years old when he died. Encourage students to start with writing down all information in "mathematical language." Suppose the age Diophantos died was a.

One-sixth of his life….	$\frac{1}{6}a$
One-twelfth more…	$\frac{1}{12}a$
One-seventh more…	$\frac{1}{7}a$
Five years passed…	$+5$
Age of son when he died	$\frac{1}{2}a$
Number of years after son's death	4

The equation that needs to be solved is:

$$\tfrac{1}{6}a + \tfrac{1}{12}a + \tfrac{1}{7}a + 5 + \tfrac{1}{2}a + 4 = a$$

A common denominator for the fractions is 84. (Note that students may also choose to multiply all terms by 84.)

$$\tfrac{14}{84}a + \tfrac{7}{84}a + \tfrac{12}{84}a + 5 + \tfrac{42}{84}a + 4 = \tfrac{84}{84}a$$

$$\tfrac{75}{84}a + 9 = \tfrac{84}{84}a$$

$$9 = \tfrac{9}{84}a$$

$$a = 84$$

Problems of Diophantos (2)

Diophantos used a fixed symbol for a variable number
or an unknown number.
This symbol looks like our letter **s**.

Here is problem 3 from the first chapter of his book.
From two numbers we know that their sum is 80.
The largest number is 3 times the smaller one plus 4.
Determine both numbers.

Here is the beginning of Diophantos's solution.
Suppose the smallest number is **s**.
Hence the larger one is 3**s** + 4.

•Complete the solution.

The two numbers are _____ and _____ .

Here is problem 5 from Diophantos's book.
From two numbers we know that their sum is 30.
5 times the first number plus 3 times the second num-
ber is equal to 100.

Suppose the first number is **s**. Then the second number
is **30 − s**.

•Complete the solution.

The two numbers are _____ and _____ .

Historic word problems

Solving linear equations using integers

- $s + 3s + 4 = 80$

  $4s + 4 = 80$

  $4s = 76$

  $s = 19$

  The two numbers are 19 and $3 \times 19 + 4 = 61$
  (Check that $61 + 19 = 80$.)

- $5s + 3(30 - s) = 100$

  $5s + 90 - 3s = 100$

  $2s + 90 = 100$

  $2s = 10$

  $s = 5$

  The two numbers are 5 and $30 - 5 = 25$
  (Check that $5 \times 5 + 3 \times 25 = 100$)

Problems of Diophantos (3)

Here is problem 6 from Diophantos's book.

From two numbers we know that their difference is 20.

6 times the smallest number plus 4 times the larger one is equal to 100.
What are those numbers?

- Complete the solution.

Suppose the smallest number is **s.**
Hence the larger number is _____ .

The two numbers are _____ and _____ .

Here is problem 7 from Diophantos's book.

Subtracting 20 from a required number the result will be 3 times the result of subtracting 100 from the same number.

What is this number?

- Solution

The required number is _____ .

Historic word problems

Solving linear equations using integers

- The larger number is $s + 20$ (Note that $(s + 20) - s = 20$.)

$6s + 4(s + 20) = 100$

$6s + 4s + 80 = 100$

$10s + 80 = 100$

$10s = 20$

$s = 2$

The two numbers are 2 and 22. (Check that $6 \times 2 + 4 \times 22 = 100$.)

- Suppose the required number is a. The equation needed to be solved is

$a - 20 = 3(a - 100)$

$a - 20 = 3a - 300$

$-20 = 2a - 300$

$280 = 2a$

$a = 140$

Table, Graph, and Formula (1)

Ronald is saving money for a mountain bike. His parents gave him $20 to start.

Suppose he saves $15 each month.

- Fill in the table and draw the corresponding graph.

Month	Amount (in dollars)
0	20
1	____
2	____
3	____
4	____
5	____

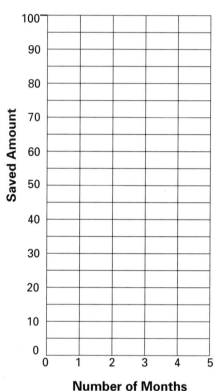

Saved Amount

Number of Months

Use **s** for the saved amount and **m** for the number of months.

- Make a formula representing the relationship between **m** and **s**.

- How does the graph change if Ronald saves $10 each month?

- What is the formula if Ronald saves $10 each month?

- How does the graph change if Ronald's parents give him $30 as a starting amount and Ronald saves $15 each month?

- What is the formula for the case above?

Use of the relationship between table, (word) formula, and graph

Linear functions

Month	Amount (in dollars)
0	20
1	35
2	50
3	65
4	80
5	95

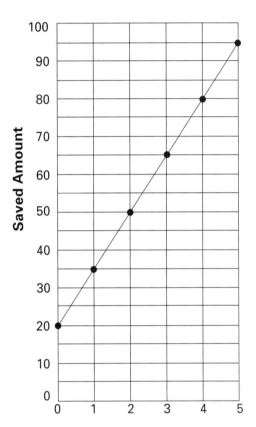

Saved Amount / **Number of Months**

Note that the graph shown here is a "dot" graph. The dots are connected by a thin straight line to show they are on a straight line. You may want to discuss with your students why a dot graph is made. The amounts are added each month; you cannot be sure this is continuous.

- $s = 20 + 15 \times m$ or $s = 20 + 15m$ or $s = 15m + 20$

The graph will be less steep if Ronald saves less per month. The starting point will stay the same.

- $s = 20 + 10 \times m$ or $s = 20 + 10m$ or $s = 10m + 20$

The steepness of the graph will stay the same, but the graph will start in point (0, 30) now.

- $s = 30 + 15 \times m$ or $s = 30 + 15m$ or $s = 15m + 30$

Table, Graph, and Formula (2)

An Internet company offers quick DSL connections that are very useful for e-mailing, surfing, and chatting.

To make the deal more attractive, the company makes an offer:

The first three months are free.

After that you pay $40 each month.

- Complete the table and draw the corresponding graph.

Months	Total Amount Paid (in dollars)
0	0
1	_____
2	_____
3	_____
4	40
5	_____
6	_____
7	_____
8	_____
9	_____
10	_____

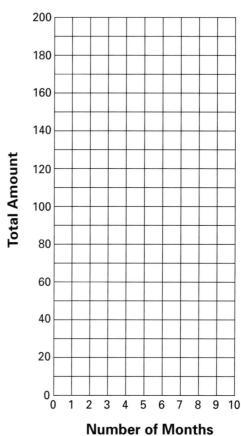

Number of Months

- After how many months is the cost $600?

Use *a* for the total amount paid and *m* for the number of months.

- Explain how the formula **a = 40(m − 3)** represents the relationship between *m* and *a* after three months.

- How does the graph change if the monthly amount is $45 and the first 4 months are free? How does the formula change in this case?

Use of the relationship between table, (word) formula, and graph

Linear functions

Months	Total Amount Paid (in dollars)
0	0
1	0
2	0
3	0
4	40
5	80
6	120
7	160
8	200
9	240
10	280

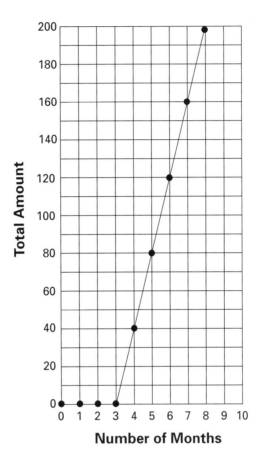

Note that the graph shown here is a "dot" graph. The dots are connected by a thin straight line to show they are on a straight line. You may want to discuss with your students why a dot graph is made. The amounts are added each month; you cannot be sure this is continuous

- After 18 months, a total amount of $600 is paid. Students may extend the table or the graph. They may also solve the equation:
  $600 = 40(m - 3)$
  $m - 3 = 15$
  $m = 18$

- If you used a DSL connection for m months, you pay for $m - 3$ months since the first three months are free. You need to multiply by 40 because you pay $40 per month.

- The graph will be steeper than the previous one, and the starting point changes from (3, 0) to (4, 0).
  The new formula will be $a = 45(m - 4)$.

Note: As an extension, you could ask after how many months the two options result in the same total amount of money paid (after 12 months), or which one is a better option if you intend to use the DSL connection more than one year (the first option).

Slopes (1)

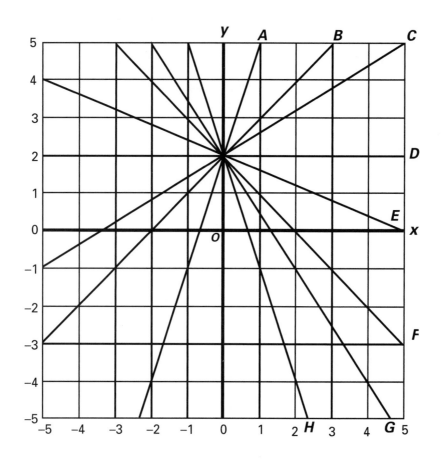

• Give the slope of each of the lines.

line	A	B	C	D	E	F	G	H
slope								

The figure with eight lines above is not symmetric.

• How many lines do you need to add to make the figure symmetric?
  What are the slopes of these lines?

Finding the slope of straight lines using a diagram

•

line	A	B	C	D	E	F	G	H
slope	3	1	$\frac{3}{5}$	0	$-\frac{2}{5}$	-1	$-\frac{3}{2} = -1\frac{1}{2}$	-3

• You need three extra lines to make the figure symmetric. The slopes of these lines are $-\frac{3}{5}, \frac{2}{5}$, and $1\frac{1}{2}$.

Slopes (2)

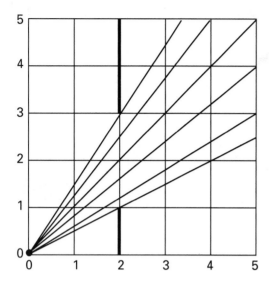

The heavy vertical line in the picture has a gap between the points (2, 1) and (2, 3).

Many rays start at the point (0, 0) and pass through that gap.

• What can you tell about the slopes of all those rays?

If you take another starting point, say (1, 0), many other rays can be drawn that pass through the gap.

• Fill in the table.

Starting Point	Slope Between
(0,1)	_____ and _____
(0,2)	_____ and _____
(0,3)	_____ and _____
(0,4)	_____ and _____
(0,5)	_____ and _____

Finding the slope of straight lines using a diagram

All slopes are between $\frac{1}{2}$ and $1\frac{1}{2}$.

The slopes of the rays passing through the gap are between 0 and 1.

The slopes are all positive.

Starting Point	Slope Between		
(0,1)	0	and	1
(0,2)	$-\frac{1}{2}$	and	$\frac{1}{2}$
(0,3)	-1	and	0
(0,4)	$-\frac{3}{2}$	and	$-\frac{1}{2}$
(0,5)	-2	and	-1

Slopes (3)

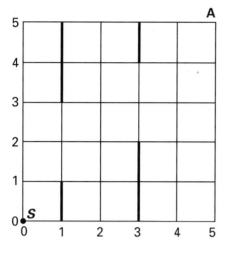

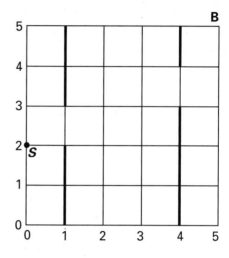

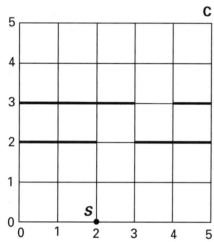

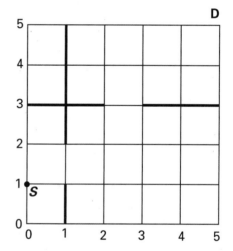

In each of the pictures you see two lines (horizontal or vertical) with a gap.

A pencil of rays starts at **S** and passes through *both* gaps.

- What is the range of the slope? Fill in the table.

Picture	Slope Between
A	_____ and _____
B	_____ and _____
C	_____ and _____
D	_____ and _____

Finding the slope of straight lines using a
diagram

Picture	Slope Between
A	_____1_____ and $\frac{4}{3} = 1\frac{1}{3}$
B	$\frac{1}{4}$ and $\frac{1}{2}$
C	_____2_____ and _____3_____
D	$\frac{2}{3}$ and _____1_____

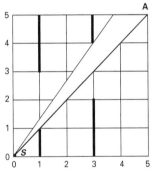

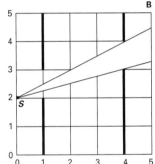

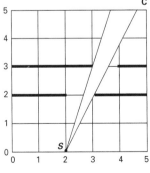

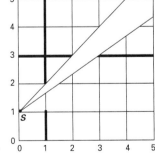

Slopes (4)

From the point (0, 0), a graph is drawn that consists of line segments with slopes 1, $\frac{1}{2}$, $\frac{1}{3}$, $\frac{1}{4}$.

The graph will be continued in this way up to and including a segment with slope $\frac{1}{10}$.

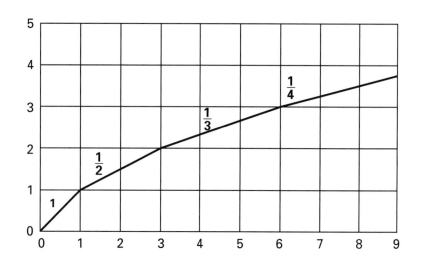

- What are the coordinates of the farthest point?

  Show your work.

Using the slope of straight lines

The farthest point is (55, 10).

Possible student work:

The first end point of a line segment is (1, 1).

For each new line, a vertical step of 1 is taken, so you end at 10.

The horizontal steps are 1, 2, 3, 4, ..., 10, so you end at $1 + 2 + 3 + 4 + 5 + 6 + 7 + 8 + 9 + 10 = 55$.

Slopes and Intercepts (1)

A line with slope $\frac{1}{2}$ passes through point **S** with coordinates (20, 18).
You can think of moving along the line one step at a time.
Each step is a move of −2 units horizontally and −1 unit vertically.

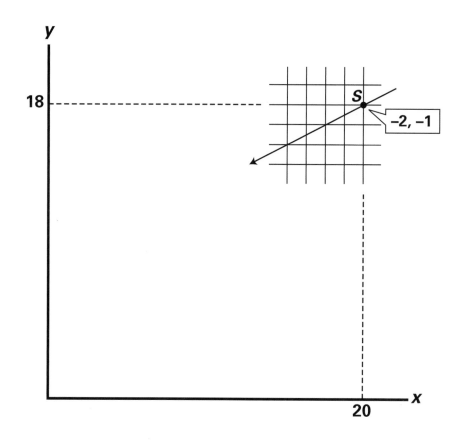

- How many steps from **S** is the y-axis?

- What number is the y-intercept of the line? Explain your answer.

- How many steps from **S** is the x-axis?

- What number is the x-intercept of the line? Explain your answer.

Finding *y*-intercept and *x*-intercept of a straight line in a geometrical way

- The *y*-axis is reached after 10 steps, because $-20 = 10 \times -2$.

- The *y*-intercept of the line is 8.

  Possible explanation:

  You move $10 \times -2 = -20$ horizontally and

  $10 \times -1 = -10$ vertically.

  $-10 + 18 = 8$

- The *x*-axis is reached in 18 steps, because $-18 = 18 \times -1$.

- The *x*-intercept of the line is -16.

  Possible explanation:

  You move $18 \times -1 = -18$ vertically and

  $18 \times -2 = -36$ horizontally.

  $-36 + 20 = -16$

Slopes and Intercepts (2)

A line with slope 3 is passing through the point **S**.

A movement along the line goes −1 unit horizontally and −3 units vertically.

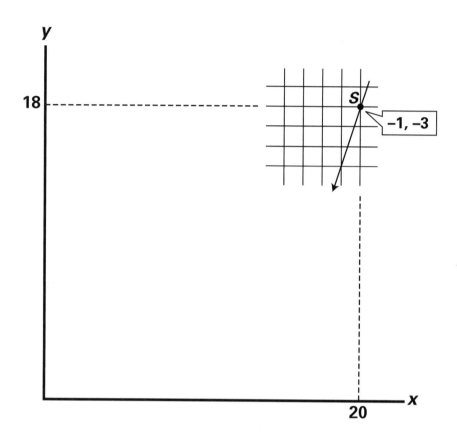

- How many steps from **S** is the x-axis?

- Which number is the x-intercept of the line?
  Explain your answer.

- How many steps from **S** is the y-axis?

- Which number is the y-intercept of the line? Explain
  your answer.

Finding *y*-intercept and *x*-intercept of a straight line in a geometrical way

- The *x*-axis is reached in six steps, because $-18 = 6 \times -3$.

  The *x*-intercept of the line is 14.

  You move 6×-3 vertically and 6×-1 horizontally.

  $-6 + 20 = 14$

- The *y*-axis is reached in 20 steps, because $20 \times -1 = -20$.

  The *y*-intercept is –42.

  You move 20×-1 horizontally and 20×-3 vertically.

  $20 \times -3 = -60$

  $-60 + 18 = -42$

Slopes and Intercepts (3)

A line is passing through the points **S** and **T** respectively with coordinates (52, 36) and (48, 35).

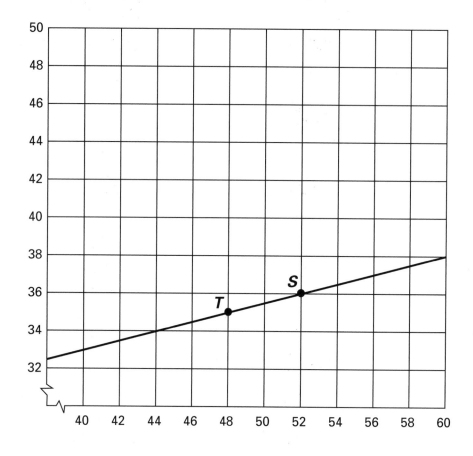

- What is the slope of line **ST**?

- Calculate the *y*-intercept and the *x*-intercept of line **ST**.

Another line passes through the points (44, 36) and (52, 34).
- What is the slope of this line?

- Calculate the *y*-intercept and the *x*-intercept of this line.

Finding slope, *y*-intercept, and *x*-intercept of a straight line in a geometrical way

- From *T* to *S* you move 4 steps in the horizontal direction and 1 step in the vertical direction. The slope is $\frac{1}{4}$.

- The *y*-intercept is 23. Starting from *T*, with each step you can make a move of −4 in the horizontal direction and −1 in the vertical direction. The *y*-axis is reached in 12 steps because 12 × −4 = −48.

  −12 + 35 = 23

  You move 12 × −4 horizontally and 12 × −1 vertically.

  The *x*-intercept of the line is −92.

  The *x*-axis is reached in 35 steps because −35 = 35 × −1.

  You move 35 × −1 vertically and 35 × −4 horizontally.

  35 × −4 = −140

  −140 + 48 = 92

- The second line has a slope of $-\frac{1}{4}$.

- The *y*-intercept is 47. Starting from the first point, with each step you can make a move of −4 in the horizontal direction and 1 in the vertical direction. The *y*-axis is reached in 11 steps. You move 11 × −4 horizontally and 11 × 1 vertically.

  The *x*-intercept of the line is 188. The *x*-axis is reached in 36 steps. You move 36 × −1 vertically and 36 × 4 horizontally.

  36 × 4 = 144

  144 + 44 = 188

Slope, Intercept, and Equation (1)

Remember:

If you know the *y*-intercept and the slope of a line, you can easily find the equation of that line.

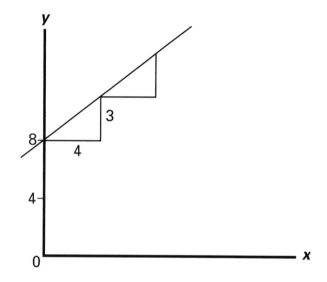

Example: *y*-intercept = 8, slope = $\frac{3}{4}$, equation: $y = 8 + \frac{3}{4}x$

• Complete the table.

slope	*y*-intercept	*x*-intercept	equation
	24	-8	
$\frac{3}{4}$	9		
$\frac{3}{4}$		−8	
	10	10	
			$y = 10 + 2x$
			$y = 2(x + 5)$
10		1	
			$y = \frac{5}{8}x$

Slope, Intercept, and Equation (1)

Relationship between slope, intercept, and equation of a straight line

slope	y-intercept	x-intercept	equation
3	24	-8	$y = 24 + 3x$
$\frac{3}{4}$	9	**-12**	$y = \frac{3}{4}x + 9$
$\frac{3}{4}$	**6**	-8	$y = \frac{3}{4}x + 6$
-1	10	10	$y = -x + 10$
2	**10**	**-5**	$y = 10 + 2x$
2	**10**	**-5**	$y = 2(x + 5)$
10	**-10**	1	$y = 10\,x - 10$
$\frac{5}{8}$	**0**	**0**	$y = \frac{5}{8}x$

Slope, Intercept, and Equation (2)

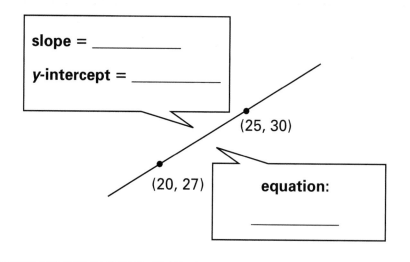

slope = _____

y-intercept = _____

(25, 30)

(20, 27)

equation:

_____

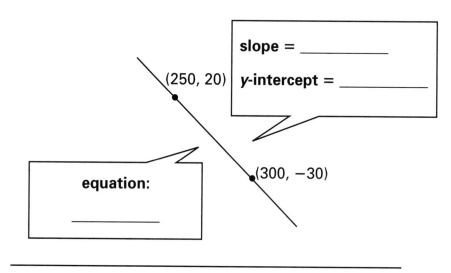

slope = _____

y-intercept = _____

(250, 20)

(300, −30)

equation:

_____

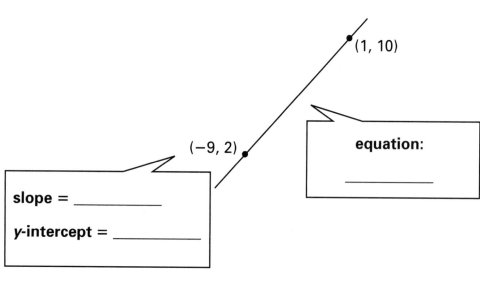

(1, 10)

(−9, 2)

equation:

_____

slope = _____

y-intercept = _____

Slope, Intercept, and Equation (2)

Relationship between slope, intercept, and equation of a straight line

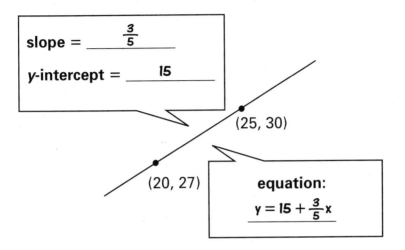

slope = $\dfrac{3}{5}$

y-intercept = 15

(25, 30)

(20, 27)

equation:

$y = 15 + \dfrac{3}{5}x$

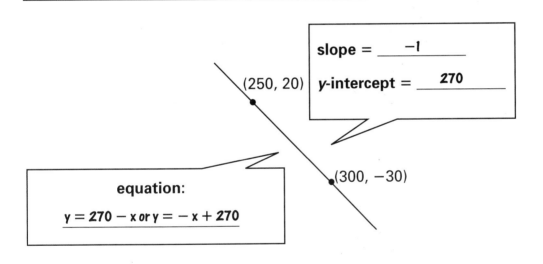

slope = −1

y-intercept = 270

(250, 20)

(300, −30)

equation:

$y = 270 - x$ or $y = -x + 270$

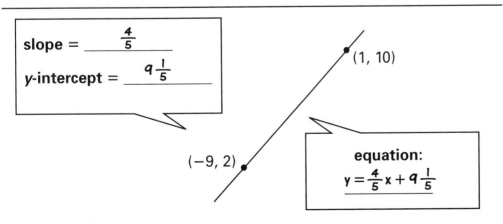

slope = $\dfrac{4}{5}$

y-intercept = $9\dfrac{1}{5}$

(1, 10)

(−9, 2)

equation:

$y = \dfrac{4}{5}x + 9\dfrac{1}{5}$

Intersecting Lines (1)

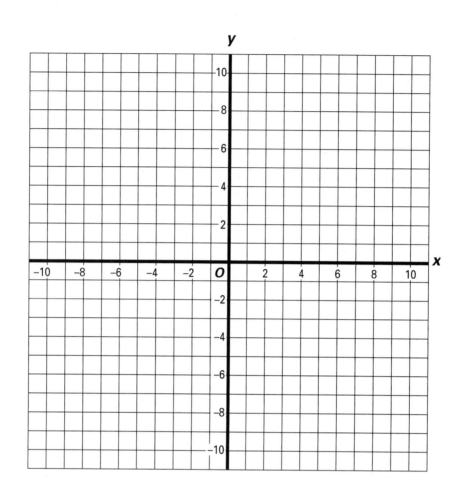

- Draw line **A** that connects the points (−2, 10) and (10, −8).

  What is the equation of that line?

- Draw line **B** that connects the points (10, 9) and (−2, −9).

- What is the equation of that line?

- Calculate the intersection point of **A** and **B**.

Intersecting Lines (1)

Finding the equation of a straight line, defined by two points

Finding the intersection point of two straight lines by solving an equation

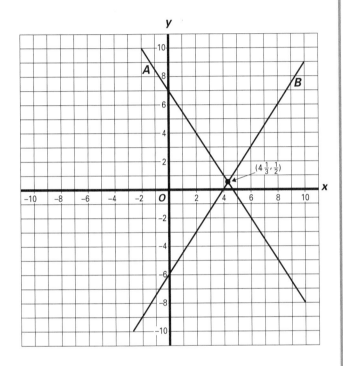

- line **A**

  slope is $-\frac{18}{12} = -1\frac{1}{2}$

  y-intercept is 7

  equation is $y = -1\frac{1}{2}x + 7$

- line **B**

  slope is $\frac{18}{12} = 1\frac{1}{2}$

  y-intercept is –6

  equation is $y = 1\frac{1}{2}x - 6$

- Note: Have students check the intersection point in their drawing after they have calculated it.

  The equation to be solved is
  $$-1\frac{1}{2}x + 7 = 1\frac{1}{2}x - 6.$$

  Subtract and set equal to zero

  $$1\frac{1}{2}x - 6$$
  $$-\frac{-1\frac{1}{2}x + 7}{3x - 13 = 0}$$
  $$3x = 13$$
  $$x = \frac{13}{3} = 4\frac{1}{3}$$
  $$y = 1\frac{1}{2} \times 4\frac{1}{3} - 6 = \frac{3}{2} \times \frac{13}{3} - 6 = \frac{1}{2}$$

  The intersection point is $(4\frac{1}{3}, \frac{1}{2})$.

Intersecting Lines (2)

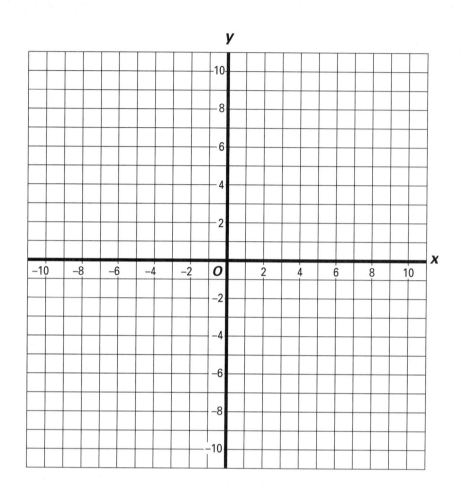

- Draw the line **C** for the equation $y = 3(x - 2\frac{1}{3})$

- What does the number $2\frac{1}{3}$ mean for that line?

- Draw line **D** for the equation $y = -2(x - 3\frac{1}{2})$

- What is the *x*-intercept of that line?

- Calculate the intersection point of **C** and **D**.

Finding the equation of a straight line, defined by two points

Finding the intersection point of two straight lines by solving an equation

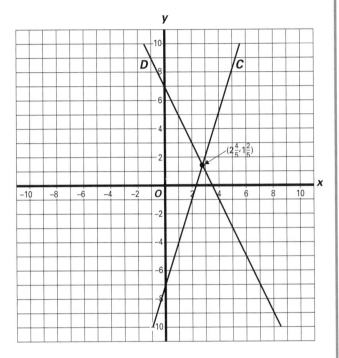

- Hint: Rewrite the equation first as $y = 3x - 7$. Students may want to make a table first. Sample table:

x	0	1	3
y	−7	−4	2

- The number $2\frac{1}{3}$ represents the x-intercept. If $x = 2\frac{1}{3}$, $y = 3 \times 2\frac{1}{3} - 7 = 0$

- Hint: rewrite the equation first as $y = -2x + 7$. Students may want to make a table first. Sample table:

x	0	1	3
y	7	5	1

- The x- intercept of the line is $3\frac{1}{2}$.

- To find the intersection point, the equation $3x - 7 = -2x + 7$ needs to be solved.

$$3x - 7$$
$$-\frac{-2x + 7}{5x = 14}$$
$$x = \frac{14}{5} = 2\frac{4}{5}$$
$$y = -2 \times 2\frac{4}{5} + 7 = 1\frac{2}{5}$$

Note: Have students check the intersection point in their drawing after they have calculated it.

Expressions and Weights (1)

$$a + a + b + b + b + c + c + c + c = 2a + 3b + 4c$$

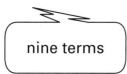

nine terms

three terms

2, 3, and 4 are the **weights** of a, b, and c.

With the weights 2, 3, and 4 and the letters a, b, and c, you can make other expressions, for example: **$4a + 3b + 2c$**.

There are six different expressions using a, b, and c with weights 2, 3, and 4.

• Write the other four expressions.

• Add the six expressions and you get a new expression with three terms. What is it?

Suppose it is known that **$c = b$**.

Now you can change **$2a + 3b + 4c$** into an expression with two terms.

$$2a + 3b + 4c$$
$$c = b$$

$$2a + 3b + 4b$$

$$2a + 7b$$

You can do the same with the other five expressions.
• How many different expressions do you get? What are they?

• If you also know that **$a = b$**, you can simplify these expressions further.

What is the result?

Showing flexibility in operations with expressions

Substitution

The role of the coefficient: formal

- $2a + 3b + 4c$ (already mentioned)

  $2a + 4b + 3c$

  $3a + 2b + 4c$

  $3a + 4b + 2c$

  $4a + 2b + 3c$

  <u>$4a + 3b + 2c$</u>   + (already mentioned)

- $18a + 18b + 18c$

Note: Have students check that the total of the weights is 9 in each expression.

    If $c = b$, there are three different expressions.

$2a + 3b + 4b = 2a + 7b$

$2a + 4b + 3b = 2a + 7b$

$3a + 2b + 4b = 3a + 6b$

$3a + 4b + 2b = 3a + 6b$

$4a + 2b + 3b = 4a + 5b$

$4a + 3b + 2b = 4a + 5b$

Note: have students check the total of the weights is 9 in each expression.

    If $a = b$, these expressions simplify to:

$2a + 7a = 9a$

$3a + 6a = 9a$

$4a + 5a = 9a$

Expressions and Weights (2)

$$w + w + x + y + y + y + y + y + z + z = 2w + x + 5y + 2z$$

w has weight 2, x has weight 1, y has weight 5, and z has weight 2.

The weight 1 is often left out in expressions, but you may want to write **$2w + 1x + 5y + 2z$.**

The sum of the weights in the expression above is 10.

- Give five other expressions in w, x, y, and z, for which the sum of the weights is equal to 10.

- Add those five expressions.
  What is the sum of the weights of the resulting expression?

If it is known that **$w = x$** and **$z = y$**, then **$2w + x + 5y + z$** can be simplified to an expression with two terms:

$$\boxed{\begin{array}{c} 2w + x + 5y + 2z \\ w = x \text{ and } z = y \end{array}}$$

$$\downarrow$$

$$\boxed{2x + x + 5y + 2y}$$

$$\downarrow$$

$$\boxed{3x + 7y}$$

- Simplify your five expressions in a similar way.

The sum of all these five expressions in x and y can also be written as an expression with two terms.
- What is it?

Showing flexibility in operations with expressions

Substitution

The role of the coefficient: formal

- Here are some examples, but there are other possibilities:

  $w + x + y + 7z$

  $2w + 2x + 2y + 4z$

  $3w + 3x + 3y + z$

  $4w + 4x + y + z$

  $5w + 2x + y + 2z$

  $6w + x + 2y + z$

  $7w + x + y + z$

Note: Have students check that the total of the weights is 10 in each expression.

- Adding five expressions:

$$
\begin{array}{r}
w + x + y + 7z \\
2w + 2x + 2y + 4z \\
3w + 3x + 3y + z \\
4w + 4x + y + z \\
+\ \underline{5w + 2x + y + 2z} \\
15w + 12x + 8y + 15z
\end{array}
$$

  The sum of the weights is $15 + 12 + 8 + 15$ $= 50$ (5×10).

- Simplifying the five expressions will lead to various answers, depending of the choices the student made. One example, $w = x$ and $z = y$:

  $w + x + y + 7z = x + x + y + 7y = 2x + 8y$

  $2w + 2x + 2y + 4z = 2x + 2x + 2y + 4y = 4x + 6y$

  $3w + 3x + 3y + z = 3x + 3x + 3y + y = 6x + 4y$

  $4w + 4x + y + z = 4x + 4x + y + y = 8x + 2y$

  $5w + 2x + y + 2z = 5x + 2x + y + 2y = 7x + 3y$

Note: Have students check that the total of the weights is 10 in each expression.

- Whatever choices were made in the previous assignment, the resulting expression in two terms is one in which the sum of the weights is 50. In our example: $27x + 23y$.

Powerful Tables (1)

Below you see a table with powers of 2.

n	2^n
0	1
1	2
2	4
3	8
4	16
5	32
6	64
7	128
8	256
9	512
10	1,024
11	2,048
12	4,096
13	8,192
14	16,384
15	32,768
16	65,536
17	131,072
18	262,144
19	524,288
20	1,048,576

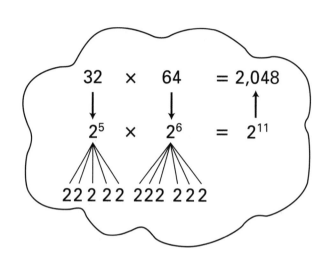

- Use the table to find the results of the following products.

  $16 \times 8{,}192 =$ _____

  $8 \times 16{,}384 =$ _____

  $512 \times 512 =$ _____

  $1{,}024 \times 1{,}024 =$ _____

- Use the table to write five different pairs of two positive integers, with a product equal to 1,048,576.

Calculations with powers

Use of the properties of powers: preformal

$16 \times 8{,}192 = 131{,}072$

$\downarrow \qquad \downarrow \qquad \uparrow$

$2^4 \times \quad 2^{13} \quad = \quad 2^{17}$

$8 \times 16{,}384 = 131{,}072$

$\downarrow \qquad \downarrow \qquad \uparrow$

$2^3 \times \quad 2^{14} \quad = \quad 2^{17}$

$512 \times 512 = 262{,}144$

$\downarrow \qquad \downarrow \qquad \uparrow$

$2^9 \quad \times \quad 2^9 \quad = \quad 2^{18}$

$1{,}024 \times 1{,}024 = 1{,}048{,}576$

$\downarrow \qquad \downarrow \qquad \uparrow$

$2^{10} \times \quad 2^{10} \quad = \quad 2^{20}$

- Many different answers are possible. As an extension, you could ask how many different possibilities there are (11).

  Some examples:

  Note that $1{,}048{,}576 = 2^{20}$

  $2 \ \times 2^{19} = 2 \times 524{,}288 = 1{,}048{,}576$

  $2^2 \times 2^{18} = 4 \times 262{,}144 = 1{,}048{,}576$

  $2^3 \times 2^{17} = 8 \times 131{,}072 = 1{,}048{,}576$

  $2^4 \times 2^{16} = 16 \times 65{,}536 = 1{,}048{,}576$

  $2^5 \times 2^{15} = 32 \times 32{,}768 = 1{,}048{,}576$

Powerful Tables (2)

The powers of 3

n	3^n
0	1
1	3
2	9
3	27
4	81
5	243
6	729
7	2187
8	6561
9	19,683
10	59,049
11	177,147
12	531,441
13	1,594,323
14	4,782,969
15	14,348,907
16	43,046,721
17	129,140,163
18	387,420,489
19	1,162,261,467
20	3,486,784,401

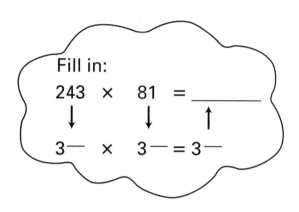

Fill in:

$243 \times 81 = $ _____

$3^— \times 3^— = 3^—$

- Find the results of the following products using the table.

  $81 \times 19,683 = $ _____

  $2,187 \times 59,049 = $ _____

  $6,561 \times 6,561 = $ _____

  $729 \times 729 \times 729 = $ _____

- Find the results of the following powers using the table.

  $81^3 = $ _____

  $243^4 = $ _____

  $27^5 = $ _____

- Which number is smaller, 9^{10} or 10^9 ? Explain.

Calculations with powers
Use of the properties of powers: preformal

- $243 \times 81 = 19{,}683$

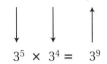

$$3^5 \times 3^4 = \quad 3^9$$

$81 \times 19{,}683 = 1{,}594{,}323$

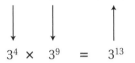

$$3^4 \times \quad 3^9 \quad = \quad 3^{13}$$

$2{,}187 \times 59{,}049 = 129{,}140{,}163$

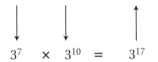

$$3^7 \quad \times \quad 3^{10} \quad = \quad 3^{17}$$

$6{,}561 \times 6{,}561 = 43{,}046{,}721$

$$3^8 \quad \times \quad 3^8 \quad = \quad 3^{16}$$

$729 \times 729 \times 729 = 387{,}420{,}489$

$$3^6 \times \quad 3^6 \times \quad 3^6 = \quad 3^{18}$$

- $81^3 = (3^4)^3 = 81 \times 81 \times 81 = 3^4 \times 3^4 \times 3^4 = 3^{12} = 531{,}441$

  $243^4 = (3^5)^4 = 243 \times 243 \times 243 \times 243 = 3^5 \times 3^5 \times 3^5 \times 3^5 = 3^{20} = 3{,}486{,}784{,}401$

  $27^5 = (3^3)^5 = 27 \times 27 \times 27 \times 27 \times 27 = 3^3 \times 3^3 \times 3^3 \times 3^3 \times 3^3 = 3^{15} = 14{,}348{,}907$

- 10^9 is smaller than 9^{10}, or $10^9 < 9^{10}$

Possible explanation:

$10^9 = 10 \times 10 \times 10 \times 10 \times 10 \times 10 \times 10 \times 10 \times 10 = 1{,}000{,}000{,}000$

$9^{10} = (3 \times 3)^{10} = 3^{20} = 3{,}486{,}784{,}401$

Powerful Tables (3)

• Make a table with powers of 5 up to 5^{10}.
  Write some problems that you can solve using this table.

n	5^n
0	1
1	5
2	
3	
4	
5	
6	
7	
8	
9	
10	

• The table with powers of 1 is very simple. Why?

• Do you know a table of powers with sharp rising results that is very easy to write? Which one?

• If you put the tables with powers of 2 and 3 next to each other, and if you multiply the numbers on the same line, then you get:

$$1 \times 1 = 1$$
$$2 \times 3 = 6$$
$$4 \times 9 = 36$$
$$8 \times 27 = 216$$
$$\ldots$$

The results are the powers of 6.
You can check this using your calculator.

• Without a calculator, explain why $2^{10} \times 3^{10} = 6^{10}$.

Calculations with powers

Use of the properties of powers: preformal

n	5^n
0	1
1	5
2	25
3	125
4	625
5	3,125
6	15,625
7	78,125
8	390,625
9	1,953,125
10	9,765,625

- Many different problems can be solved using this table. Some examples:
  $25 \times 125 = 5^2 \times 5^3 = 5^5 = 3,125$
  $25 \times 25 \times 25 \times 25 = 5^2 \times 5^2 \times 5^2 \times 5^2 = 5^8 = 390,625$
  $125^3 = (5^3)^3 = 5^3 \times 5^3 \times 5^3 = 1,953,125$
  $3,125 \times 3,125 = 5^5 \times 5^5 = 5^{10} = 9,765,625$

- The table of powers of one is simple because all results are one.
  $1^0 = 1$
  $1^1 = 1$
  $1^2 = 1 \times 1 = 1$
  $1^3 = 1 \times 1 \times 1 = 1$
  $1^{100} = 1$

- A table of powers that is easy to write is the table of powers of ten.
  $10^0 = 1$
  $10^1 = 10$
  $10^2 = 100$
  $10^3 = 1,000$
  $10^4 = 10,000$
  $10^5 = 100,000$

- $2^{10} \times 3^{10} = 6^{10}$ Possible explanation, using a simpler example:

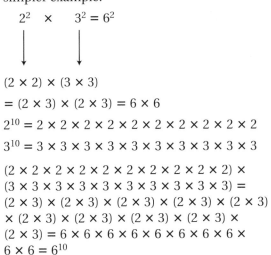

$$2^2 \quad \times \quad 3^2 = 6^2$$

$(2 \times 2) \times (3 \times 3)$
$= (2 \times 3) \times (2 \times 3) = 6 \times 6$
$2^{10} = 2 \times 2 \times 2 \times 2 \times 2 \times 2 \times 2 \times 2 \times 2 \times 2$
$3^{10} = 3 \times 3 \times 3 \times 3 \times 3 \times 3 \times 3 \times 3 \times 3 \times 3$

$(2 \times 2 \times 2 \times 2 \times 2 \times 2 \times 2 \times 2 \times 2 \times 2) \times$
$(3 \times 3 \times 3 \times 3 \times 3 \times 3 \times 3 \times 3 \times 3 \times 3) =$
$(2 \times 3) \times (2 \times 3) \times (2 \times 3) \times (2 \times 3) \times (2 \times 3)$
$\times (2 \times 3) \times (2 \times 3) \times (2 \times 3) \times (2 \times 3) \times$
$(2 \times 3) = 6 \times 6 \times 6 \times 6 \times 6 \times 6 \times 6 \times 6 \times$
$6 \times 6 = 6^{10}$

Operating with Powers (1)

$$a \times a \times a \times b \times b \times c = a^3 \times b^2 \times c^1 = a^3 b^2 c$$

The exponents of *a*, *b*, and *c* are 3, 2, and 1.

(Note: The exponent 1 is usually not written.)

With the exponents 3, 2, and 1 and the letters *a*, *b*, and *c*, other products also can be made, for example, ab^3c^2.

Six products can be made using *a*, *b*, and *c* and the exponents 1, 2, and 3.

• Write the other four products.

• Multiply the six products together.
  The result can be written in the form $a{-}b{-}c{-}$.
  Which exponents do you get?

If **b** = **a**, you can simplify a^3b^2c.

```
┌───────────────────────┐
│      a³ b² c          │
│      b = a            │
└───────────┬───────────┘
            ▼
┌───────────────────────┐
│      a³ a² c          │
└───────────┬───────────┘
            ▼
┌───────────────────────┐
│      a⁵ c             │
└───────────────────────┘
```

You can do the same with the other five products.

• How many different products do you get? Which ones?

• If you also know that **c** = **a**, you can write each of these products as a *power* of **a**. Which one?

Operating with Powers (1)

Flexibility in calculations with powers

Substitution: formal

- ab^2c^3

  a^2b^3c

  a^2bc^3

  a^3bc^2

- $ab^3c^2 \times ab^2c^3 \times a^2b^3c \times a^2bc^3 \times a^3b^2c \times a^3bc^2$
  $= a^{12}b^{12}c^{12}$

  The exponents of a, b, and c are 12.

- ab^2c^3 $b = a$ $aa^2c^3 = a^3c^3$

  ab^3c^2 $b = a$ $aa^3c^2 = a^4c^2$

  a^2b^3c $b = a$ $a^2a^3c = a^5c$

  a^2bc^3 $b = a$ $a^2ac^3 = a^3c^3$

  a^3bc^2 $b = a$ $a^3ac^2 = a^4c^2$

  There are three different products: a^5c, a^4c^2, and a^3c^3.

- If $c = a$, the three different products a^5c, a^4c^2, and a^3c^3 changes into a^6.

Operating with Powers (2)

$$2m^3 \times 3m^2 = 2 \times 3 \times m^5 = 6m^5$$

$2 \times m \times m \times m$ $3 \times m \times m$

- Find as many other multiplications as possible with the same result.

_____ x _____ = $6m^5$

_____ x _____ = $6m^5$

_____

_____

_____

_____

_____

_____

_____

Flexibility in calculations with powers: formal

$2m^3 \times 3m^2 = 6m^5$

Other multiplications with the same result, in no particular order. Other multiplications are possible.

$m^3 \times 6m^2 = 6m^5$ Note that m^3 is equal to $1 \times m^3$ or $1m^3$

$6m^3 \times m^2 = 6m^5$

$3m^3 \times 2m^2 = 6m^5$

$4m^3 \times 1\frac{1}{2}m^2 = 6m^5$

$1\frac{1}{2}m^3 \times 4m^2 = 6m^5$

$2m^2 \times 3m^3 = 6m^5$

$2m \times 3m^4 = 6m^5$

$3m^2 \times 2m^3 = 6m^5$

$6m \times m^4 = 6m^5$

$\frac{1}{3}m^2 \times 18m^3 = 6m^5$

$6m^2 \times m^3 = 6m^5$

$18m \times \frac{1}{3}m^4 = 6m^5$

$2 \times 3m^5 = 6m^5$

Dot Patterns (1)

Nicomachos lived in Greece in about the year 100 A.D.

He wrote a book about what he called the "admirable and divine properties" of whole numbers.

Nicomachos sometimes used dots to represent numbers.

Below you see the most famous examples.

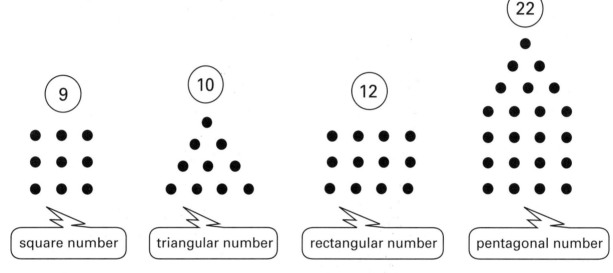

| square number | triangular number | rectangular number | pentagonal number |

He gave every type a geometrical name.

To begin with, consider the family of the **square numbers**.

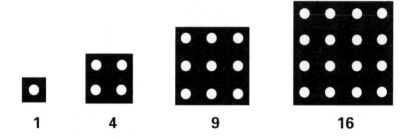

1   **4**   **9**   **16**

- Write the next ten square numbers. You do not need to draw the corresponding patterns, but you can "see" them in your mind.

- Consider the steps between successive square numbers. Do you see any rule? How can you see that rule in the dot pattern?

- 144 is a square number. Is 1,444 a square number? Is 14,444? Use a calculator to investigate this.

Geometric representation of square numbers

Finding a pattern

- The next ten square numbers are: 25 36 49 64 81 100 121 144 169 196

- The steps between successive square numbers (including 1, 4, 9, 16) are: 3 5 7 9 11 13 15 17 19 21......

These are successive odd numbers.

In the dot patterns, you can see this by looking at the part that was added to the previous number:

three dots are added to the first square number, which consisted of one dot.

five dots are added to the previous square number, which consisted of four dots.

- 144 is a square number, consisting of 12 × 12 dots

  1,444 is a square number, consisting of 38 × 38 dots

  14,444 is *not* a square number because it is between the answers of:

  120 × 120 = 14,400

  121 × 121 = 14,641

Dot Patterns (2)

These are the first four **rectangular numbers**.

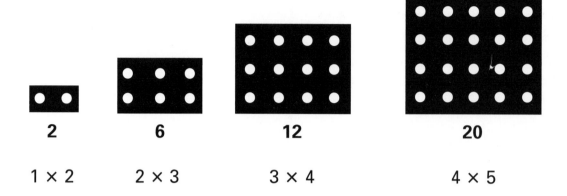

2	**6**	**12**	**20**
1 × 2	2 × 3	3 × 4	4 × 5

- Write the next ten rectangular numbers. Continue the dot pattern in your mind.

- Consider the steps between successive rectangular numbers.
  Do you see any rule? How can you see that rule in the dot patterns?

- Is 9,900 a rectangular number? Explain your answer.

Take the mean of pairs of successive rectangular numbers.

    the mean of 2 and 6 is 4

    the mean of 6 and 12 is 9

    the mean of 12 and 20 is 16

- Continue this at least 5 more times.
  Which special numbers do you get as a result?
  Try to explain your discovery.

Geometric representation of rectangular numbers
Finding a pattern

- The next ten rectangular numbers are: 30, 42, 56, 72, 90, 110, 132, 156, 182, 210.

- The pattern of dots increases by a row and column each time. The steps between successive rectangular numbers are: 4, 6, 8, 10, 12, 14, 16, 18, …; these are successive even numbers.

- 9,900 is indeed a rectangular number.

Possible explanations:

- You can write 9,900 as 99 × 100 and all rectangular numbers can be written as the product of two successive whole numbers.

- You can find a rectangular number by taking a square number and adding one extra column: the third square number

one extra column added to the square number gives the third rectangular number.

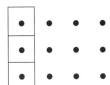

Now, by trial and error, you find that 9,801 is a square number (99 × 99). Adding one column of 99 will give you a rectangular number, 9,801 + 99 = 9,900.

- The mean of 2 and 6 is 4.
  The mean of 6 and 12 is 9.
  The mean of 12 and 20 is 16.
  The mean of 20 and 30 is 25   20 = 4 × 5 and
  The mean of 30 and 42 is 36.   30 = 6 × 5, so
  The mean of 42 and 56 is 49.   the mean is 5 × 5.
  The mean of 56 and 72 is 64.
  The mean of 72 and 90 is 81.
  As a result, you get a sequence of square numbers.
  Possible explanation:
  Add two rectangular numbers, for instance 12 and 20.

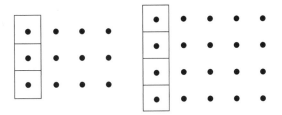

Now add the two rectangles and divide in two equal parts.

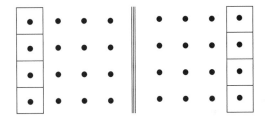

The result are two squares.

Note: Some students may give an algebraic explanation: The nth rectangular pattern can be described as $n^2 + n$. The next rectangular pattern is $(n + 1)^2 + (n + 1)$.

Adding the two expressions results in

$n^2 + n + (n + 1)^2 + (n + 1) = n^2 + n + n^2 + 2n + 1 + n + 1 =$

$2n^2 + 4n + 2$.

Dividing by two:

$n^2 + 2n + 1 = (n + 1)^2$, which is a square number.

Or:

Each rectangular number can be written as the product of two successive whole numbers

$n(n - 1)$. The next rectangular number is $n(n + 1)$

$n(n - 1) = n^2 - n$

$n(n + 1) = n^2 + n$

The mean of these two numbers is n^2.

Dot Patterns (3)

Nicomachos was not the first person who used dot patterns for numbers.

Pythagoras lived 600 years earlier (about 500 B.C.). He was a scholar who was the leader of a religious sect.

In the doctrine of Pythagoras, "whole numbers" played a leading part.

He and his disciples had a favorite expression: "Everything is number."

Their favorite number was 10, which is the sum of 1, 2, 3, and 4.

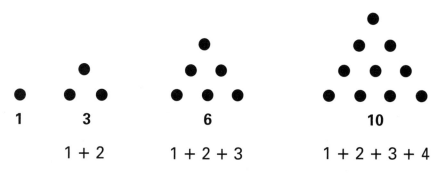

Ten is the fourth number in the sequence of the **triangular numbers**.
 • Write the next ten triangular numbers.

The dot patterns of the triangular numbers can also be drawn this way.

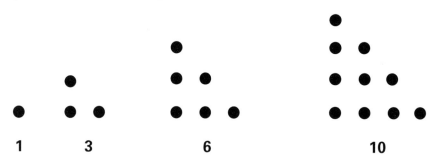

 • Which special numbers do you get if each of the triangular numbers are doubled? How can you explain this using the dot patterns?

 • Is 4,950 a triangular number? Explain your answer.

Geometric representation of triangular numbers

Finding a pattern

Historic link

- The next ten triangular numbers are: 15 21 28 36 45 55 66 78 91 105.

- You get rectangular numbers if you double the triangular numbers. Each dot pattern, as shown, is half of a rectangular number.

●	*	*	*
●	●	*	*
●	●	●	*

- Yes, 4,950 is a triangular number. You may recall in Dot Patterns (2) that $2 \times 4{,}950 = 9{,}900$ is a rectangular number. So half of it is a triangular number.

  Or students may recall that 9,900 is a rectangular number and so $\frac{1}{2} \times 9{,}900 = 4{,}950$, which is $\frac{1}{2}$ of a rectangular number or a triangular number.

Strips and Dots (1)

square numbers   *rectangular numbers*

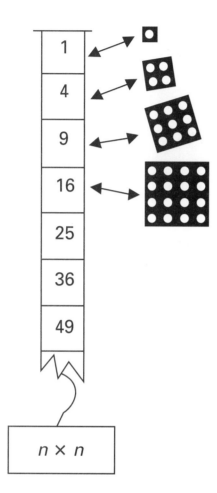
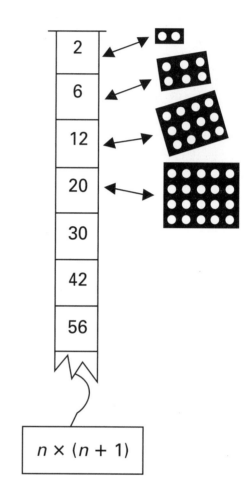

The expression for the square numbers is usually written as n^2 and read as **n squared**.

- Compare both strips. What strip can you add to the left one to get the right one?

The expressions $n \times (n + 1)$ and $n^2 + n$ are equivalent.

- How can you explain this using dot patterns?

Adding and multiplying polynomials

Equivalent expressions

• You can add the strip with expression n.

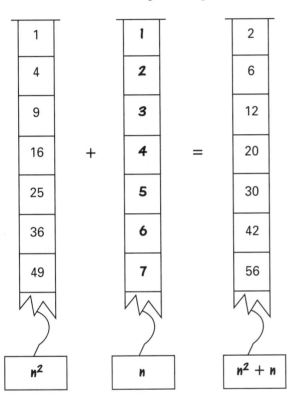

Look at this example from Dot Patterns (2). column:

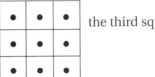

the third square number 3×3.

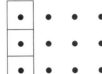

the third rectangular number, $3 \times 3 + 3$.

In general, if you add n to the square number $n \times n$, the result is a rectangular number,

$n \times n + n$ or $n(n + 1)$.

Strips and Dots (2)

triangular numbers   *rectangular numbers*

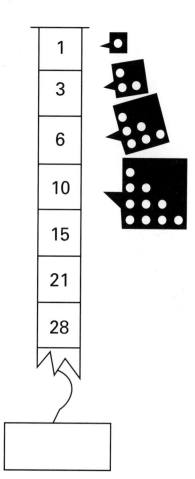
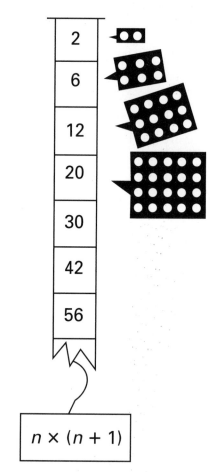

$n \times (n + 1)$

Compare the triangular numbers with the rectangular numbers.

- What expression fits the strip of triangular numbers?

- Give one (or more) equivalent expressions.

Using the expression for triangular numbers, calculate the sum of the first hundred positive whole numbers.

$1 + 2 + 3 + 4 + 5 + \ldots + 98 + 99 + 100 =$ _____

Finding quadratic expressions

Equivalent expressions

- Recall you could find the rectangular numbers by doubling the triangular numbers. The expression that fits the strip with the triangular numbers is $\frac{1}{2} \times n \times (n + 1)$.

  Examples of equivalent expressions are

  $\frac{1}{2}n^2 + \frac{1}{2}n$ and

  $$\frac{n \times (n + 1)}{2} \text{ and}$$

  $$\frac{n^2 + n}{2}$$

  Some others are:

  $\frac{1}{2} \times n \times (n + 1) = \frac{1}{2}(n^2 + n)$

  $\frac{n^2}{2} + \frac{n}{2} = \frac{n}{2}(n + 1)$

- The sum of the first hundred positive whole numbers ($n = 100$) is the hundredth triangular number:
  $\frac{1}{2} \times 100 \times (100 + 1) = 50 \times 101 = 5{,}050.$

Strips and Dots (3)

triangular numbers   **pentagonal numbers**

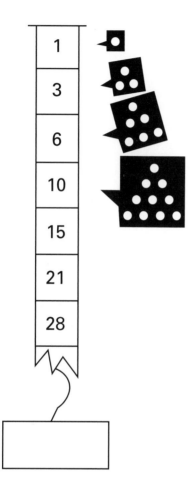

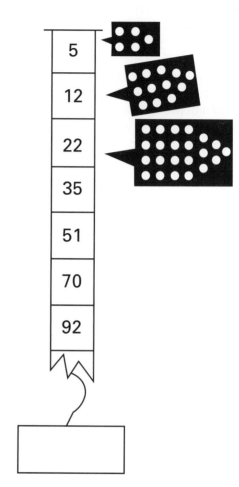

Compare the numbers of both strips.

- Which pentagonal number is right after 92?

- Find an expression that represents the sequence of pentagonal numbers.

Finding quadratic expressions

Equivalent expressions

- 117 is the pentagonal number that succeeds 92.

  Look at the pattern in the strip. You add a square to each triangular number.

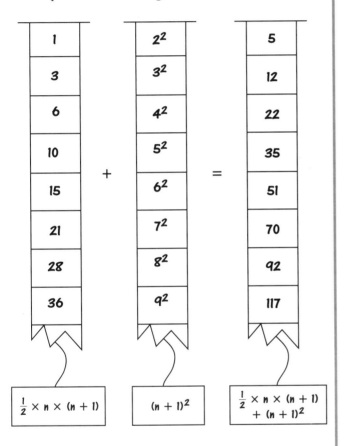

$\frac{1}{2} \times n \times (n + 1)$ $(n + 1)^2$ $\frac{1}{2} \times n \times (n + 1) + (n + 1)^2$

- An expression which represents the sequence of pentagonal numbers is:

$$\frac{1}{2} \times n \times (n + 1) + (n + 1)^2$$

Note that it is often unclear how you find the expression if you simplify the result. That is why we do not recommend simplifying the expression.

Number Spirals (1)

You can make a number line in the shape of a spiral!

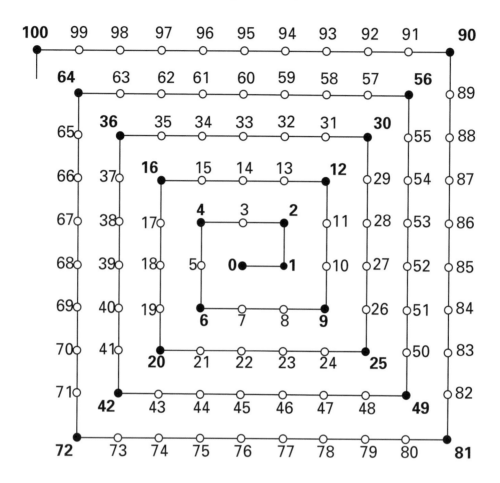

The black vertices of the spiral correspond with special families of numbers.

• Which families?

In the diagram, you can see that every square number is exactly between two rectangular numbers.

For example, **49** is between **42** and **56**.

This is because **49 = 7 × 7** and **42 = 6 × 7** and **56 = 8 × 7**.

• The square number 144 lies in the middle between the rectangular numbers _____ and _____ .

• The square number 1,444 lies in the middle between the rectangular numbers _____ and _____ .

• The square number n^2 lies in the middle between the rectangular numbers _____ and _____ .

Exploring patterns in numbers

Using square and rectangular numbers

- Rectangular numbers and square numbers.
- The square number 144 (12 × 12) lies in the middle between the rectangular numbers 132 (11 × 12) and 156 (13 × 12).
- The square number 1444 (38 × 38) lies in the middle between the rectangular numbers 1406 (37 × 38) and 1482 (39 × 38).
- The square number n^2 ($n \times n$) lies in the middle between the rectangular numbers $n^2 - n$; $[(n - 1) \times n]$ and $n^2 + n$; $[(n + 1) \times n]$.

Number Spirals (2)

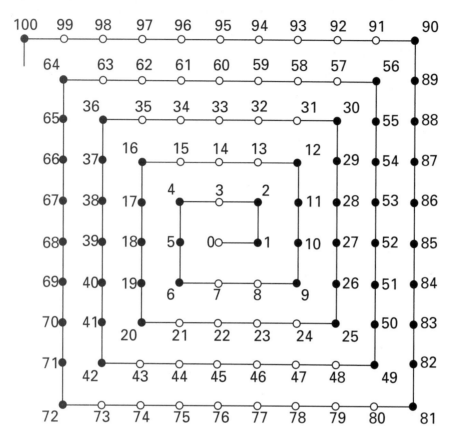

The dots on the vertical parts of the number spiral are black, and the others dots are white. If you add the black numbers from one vertical part, the result is equal to the sum of the next set of larger white numbers.

You can check that.

$$1 + 2 = 3$$
$$4 + 5 + 6 = 7 + 8$$
$$9 + 10 + 11 + 12 = 13 + 14 + 15$$
$$16 + 17 + 18 + 19 + 20 = 21 + 22 + 23 + 24$$

- What is the next line of this pattern?
- You can check this line without calculating both sums. (Hint: Mark the steps from "black" to "white.")

Line **n** begins with the black number **n²**.

- Give an expression for the last black number on that line.

(Hint: How many steps to the end of the black line starting with 25? How many to the end of the black line starting with 64?)

Exploring patterns in numbers

Relating the patterns to quadratic formulas

- **25 + 26 + 27 + 28 + 29 + 30** = 31 + 32 + 33 + 34 + 35

- From **25** to 31, there are six steps.

  From **26** to 32, there are six steps.

  From **27** to 33, there are six steps.

  From **28** to 34, there are six steps.

  From **29** to 35, there are six steps.

  From **31** ("white" side) there are $5 \times 6 = 30$ steps "extra," which is just equal to the 30 on the "black" side.

- From 25 to 30 there are 5 steps.

  From 36 to 42 there are 6 steps.

  From 64 to 72 there are 8 steps.

  The first line starts with 1^2, the second line with 2^2, the third line with 3^2, and so on. So the nth line starts with n^2.

  The first line has one step to the last number; the second line has two steps; the third line has three steps; and so on. So the nth line has n steps to the last number.

  Starting with n^2 there are n steps to the last black number. So last black number is $n^2 + n$ or $n \times n + n$.

Strips and Expressions (1)

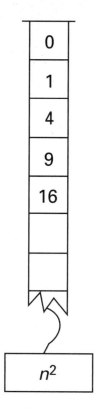

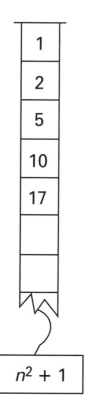

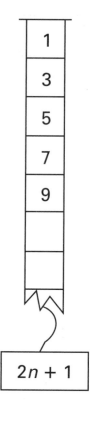

0	1	1	1
1	4	2	3
4	9	5	5
9	16	10	7
16	25	17	9

n^2 $(n + 1)^2$ $n^2 + 1$ $2n + 1$

• Are these equivalent?

n^2	$\overset{?}{=}$	$n \times n$		$2n + 1$	$\overset{?}{=}$	$n \times n + 1$

$n^2 + 1$	$\overset{?}{=}$	$n^2 + 1^2$		$2(n + 1)$	$\overset{?}{=}$	$2n + 1$

$(n + 1)^2$	$\overset{?}{=}$	$n^2 + 1^2$		$(n + 1)^2$	$\overset{?}{=}$	$n^2 + 2n + 1$

$n^2 + 1$	$\overset{?}{=}$	$n \times n + 1 \times 1$		$(n + 1)^2$	$\overset{?}{=}$	$n^2 + 1 + 2n$

Strips and Expressions (1)

Equivalent quadratic expressions: preformal, formal

Students can use strips to check their answers.

$n^2 = n \times n$ equivalent

$n^2 + 1 = n^2 + 1^2$ equivalent

$(n + 1)^2 \ne n^2 + 1^2$ *not* equivalent

If you replace n by 2, the result is $(2 + 1)^2$ $\ne 2^2 + 1^2$ or $9 \ne 5$.

$n^2 + 1 = n \times n + 1 \times 1$ equivalent

$2n + 1 \ne n \times n + 1$ *not* equivalent

If you replace n by 5, the result is 2×5 $\ne 5 \times 5 + 1$ or $10 \ne 26$.

$2(n + 1) \ne 2n + 1$ *not* equivalent

If you replace n by 3, the result is $2(3 + 1)$ $\ne 2 \times 3 + 1$ or $8 \ne 7$.

Note that $2(n + 1)$ is equivalent with $2n + 2$, which is one more than $2n + 1$.

$(n + 1)^2 = n^2 + 2n + 1$ equivalent

$(n + 1)^2 = n^2 + 1 + 2n$ equivalent

Note: If expressions are *not* equivalent, giving just *one* counterexample is enough.

Strips and Expressions (2)

• Fill in the missing numbers and expressions.

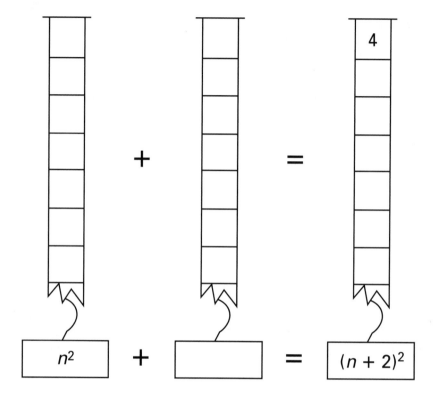

$$n^2 \quad + \quad \boxed{} \quad = \quad (n + 2)^2$$

0			25
1			36
4			49
9			64
16			81
25			100
36			121

$$n^2 \quad + \quad \boxed{} \quad = \quad \boxed{}$$

Equivalent quadratic expressions: preformal

Note that n starts at zero in the strips.

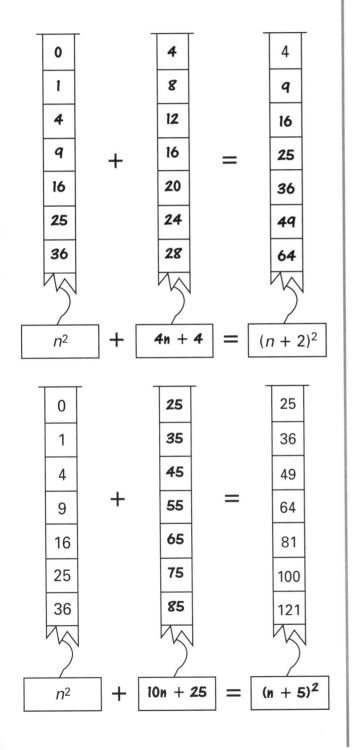

Formulas About Squares

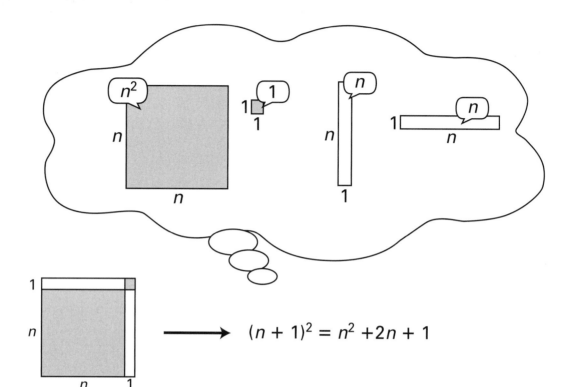

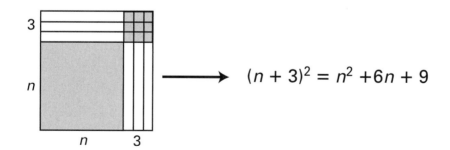

$(n + 1)^2 = n^2 + 2n + 1$

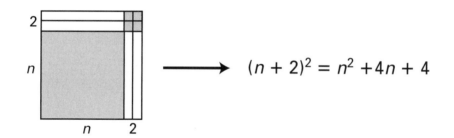

$(n + 2)^2 = n^2 + 4n + 4$

$(n + 3)^2 = n^2 + 6n + 9$

• How will this sequence continue? Write the next five formulas.

Formulas about Squares

Equivalent quadratic expressions

Geometric representation: formal

$(n + 4)^2 = n^2 + 8n + 16$

$(n + 5)^2 = n^2 + 10n + 25$

$(n + 6)^2 = n^2 + 12n + 36$

$(n + 7)^2 = n^2 + 14n + 49$

$(n + 8)^2 = n^2 + 16n + 64$

Name _____   Date_____   Class_____

Always a Square?

$$1 \times 3 + 1 = 4$$
$$2 \times 4 + 1 = 9$$
$$3 \times 5 + 1 = 16$$
$$4 \times 6 + 1 = 25$$
$$5 \times 7 + 1 = 36$$
$$6 \times 8 + 1 = 49$$

_____

_____

_____

_____

Look at the pattern.
- Write the next four calculations.

The result of each calculation seems to be a square number.
- Try to say what is going on.

- Complete:

    $29 \times 31 + 1 = $ _____

    _____ $\times$ _____ $+ 1 = 2{,}500$

- Write a formula that represents all these calculations:

    $n \times$ _____ $+ 1 = $ _____ .

- How can you explain this formula?

Mathematics in Context

Always a Square?

Working with quadratic formulas

Equivalent quadratic expressions: preformal, formal

$$1 \times 3 + 1 = 4$$
$$2 \times 4 + 1 = 9$$
$$3 \times 5 + 1 = 16$$
$$4 \times 6 + 1 = 25$$
$$5 \times 7 + 1 = 36$$
$$6 \times 8 + 1 = 49$$
$$7 \times 9 + 1 = 64$$
$$8 \times 10 + 1 = 81$$
$$9 \times 11 + 1 = 100$$
$$10 \times 12 + 1 = 121$$

- You multiply a number by the same number plus two, you add an extra one and the result seems to always be a square number.

- $29 \times 31 + 1 = (30 \times 30)$

  $49 \times 51 + 1 = 2{,}500$

- Hint: Look at the formulas about squares on the previous page!

  $n \times (n + 2) + 1 = (n + 1)^2$

- You can show the formula is right by finding equivalent expressions:

  $n \times (n + 2) + 1 = n^2 + 2n + 1 = (n + 1)^2$

Rectangular Multiplying (1)

$$32 \times 38 = 30 \times 30 + 10 \times 30 + 2 \times 8 = 1{,}216$$

$$\underbrace{}_{900} \quad \underbrace{}_{300} \quad \underbrace{}_{16}$$

This shows an example of smart multiplying.

- How can you explain this method by using a 38 × 32 rectangle?

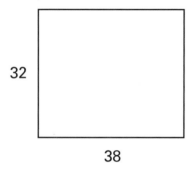

- Calculate in the same way:

24 × 26 = _____ + _____ + _____ = _____

43 × 47 = _____ + _____ + _____ = _____

61 × 69 = _____ + _____ + _____ = _____

75 × 75 = _____ + _____ + _____ = _____

- Explain at least one of these multiplications by a rectangle.

- Using two numbers between 10 and 100, write three other multiplications you can calculate in the same smart way.

Use of distributive property using numbers: preformal

Rectangular model for multiplying

- The rectangle shows 8 × 30 and 2 × 30 can be taken together as 10 × 30.

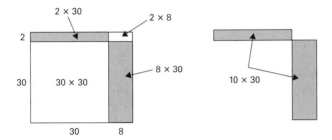

- 24 × 26 = 20 × 20 + 10 × 20 + 4 × 6 = 400 + 200 + 24 = 624 Have students check the answer by making the calculation in any other way.

  43 × 47 = 40 × 40 + 10 × 40 + 3 × 7 = 1,600 + 400 + 21 = 2,021

  61 × 69 = 60 × 60 + 10 × 60 + 1 × 9 = 3,600 + 600 + 9 = 4,209

  75 × 75 = 70 × 70 + 10 × 70 + 5 × 5 = 4,900 + 700 + 25 = 5,625

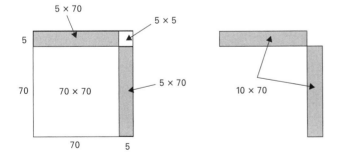

- Students' own multiplications will vary. The rule only works if the second digits add up to ten.

Rectangular Multiplying (2)

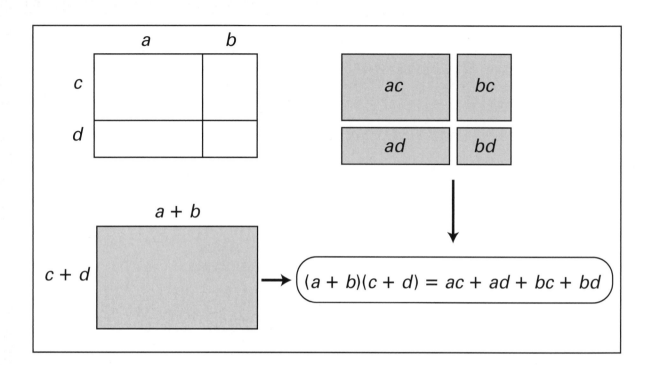

The diagram shows an algebra rule:

The product of the sums $a + b$ and $c + d$ is equal to the sum of the products $ac, ad, bc,$ and bd.

- Use this rule to calculate:

  $43 \times 57 = (40 + 3) \times (50 + 7) =$ _____ $=$ _____

  $47 \times 53 =$ _____ $=$ _____ $=$ _____

- Use the same rule to calculate:

  $102 \times 104 =$ _____

  $201 \times 401 =$ _____

  $25 \times 35 + 25 \times 65 + 75 \times 35 + 75 \times 65 = 10,000$

- How can you check this answer without calculating the four products?

- Calculate in a smart way.

  $145 \times 11 + 145 \times 89 + 55 \times 11 + 55 \times 89$

- Explain by using rectangles that the expressions

  $(u + v)(x + y + z)$ and $ux + uy + uz + vx + vy + vz$ are equivalent.

Use of distributive property using numbers and variables in a rectangle model: formal

- $43 \times 57 = (40 + 3) \times (50 + 7)$

  $= 40 \times 50 + 40 \times 7 + 3 \times 50 + 3 \times 7$

  $= 2{,}000 + 280 + 150 + 21 = 2{,}451$

- $47 \times 53 = (40 + 7) \times (50 + 3)$

  $= 40 \times 50 + 40 \times 3 + 7 \times 50 + 7 \times 3$

  $= 2{,}000 + 120 + 350 + 21 = 2{,}491$

- $102 \times 104 = (100 + 2) \times (100 + 4)$

  $= 100 \times 100 + 100 \times 4 + 2 \times 100 + 2 \times 4$

  $= 10{,}000 + 400 + 200 + 8 = 10{,}608$

- $201 \times 401 = (200 + 1) \times (400 + 1)$

  $= 200 \times 400 + 200 \times 1 + 1 \times 400 + 1 \times 1$

  $= 80{,}000 + 200 + 400 + 1 = 80{,}601$

- Check the answers by using a smart way to group the multiplications. You may wish to tell your students this is possible because the distributive property holds here.

$25 \times 35 + 75 \times 35 =$
$(25 + 75) \times 35 =$
100×35

$25 \times 65 + 75 \times 65 =$
$(25 + 75) \times 65 =$
100×65

$+$

$100 \times 35 + 100 \times 65 =$
$100 \times (35 + 65) =$
$100 \times 100 =$
$10{,}000$

- $145 \times 11 + 145 \times 89 + 55 \times 11 + 55 \times 89$

  $= 145 \times 100 + 55 \times 100$

  $= 200 \times 100 = 20{,}000$

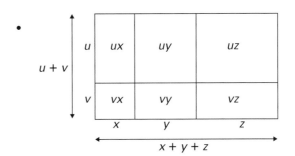

Rectangular Multiplying (3)

• Fill in the blanks for each rectangle.

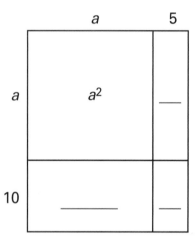

$(a + 5) (c + 10) =$

$ac +$ ____ $+$ ____ $+$ ____

$(a + 5) (a + 10) =$

$a^2 +$ ____ $+$ ____ $+$ ____

The last expression can be simplified to an expression with only three terms.

• How?

The expressions $(x + 3)(x + 7)$ and $x^2 + 10x + 21$ are equivalent.

• Explain why.

• Which pairs of expressions are equivalent? Explain your answers.

$(a + 4)(b + 6)$ and $ab + 24$

$(a + 4)(a + 6)$ and $a^2 + 10a + 24$

$(b + 4)(b + 6)$ and $b(b + 10) + 24$

Using distributive property using numbers and variables in a rectangle model: formal

Similar terms

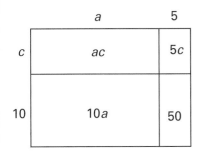

$(a + 5)(c + 10) =$
$ac + 10a + 5c + 50$

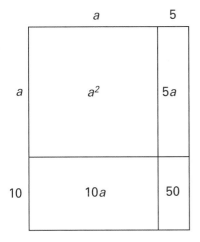

$(a + 5)(a + 10) =$
$a^2 + 10a + 5a + 50$

- The expression can be simplified by adding the two similar terms.

$a^2 + 10a + 5a + 50 = a^2 + 15a + 50$

- $(x + 3)(x + 7) = x^2 + 7x + 3x + 21 =$
$x^2 + 10x + 21$

You may want to encourage students to make rectangles to show whether the expressions are equivalent.

	x	7
x	x^2	$7x$
3	$3x$	21

- $(a + 4)(b + 6) = ab + 6a + 4b + 24$, which is *not* equivalent with $ab + 24$.

  $(a + 4)(a + 6) = a^2 + 6a + 4a + 24 =$
  $a^2 + 10a + 24$; the expressions are equivalent.

  $(b + 4)(b + 6) = b^2 + 6b + 4b + 24 =$
  $b^2 + 10b + 24$

  $b(b + 10) + 24 = b^2 + 10b + 24$ the expressions are equivalent.

Name _____ Date_____ Class_____

You Can Count on It (1)

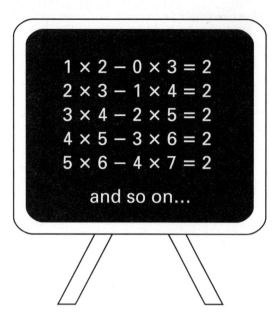

$$1 \times 2 - 0 \times 3 = 2$$
$$2 \times 3 - 1 \times 4 = 2$$
$$3 \times 4 - 2 \times 5 = 2$$
$$4 \times 5 - 3 \times 6 = 2$$
$$5 \times 6 - 4 \times 7 = 2$$

and so on...

- Check the calculations on the blackboard. Continue the sequence with some more lines. What do you think?

- Use numbers between 100 and 1,000 to give some other calculations that fit in the sequence. Check to see if the result is 2.

This is the general rule.

$$(n + 1) \times (n + 2) - n \times (n + 3) = 2$$

- Use the pictures in the cloud to explain that this is true.

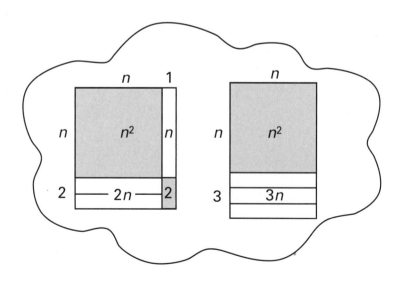

Relating patterns in numbers to quadratic expressions

Equivalent quadratic expressions: preformal, formal

- $6 \times 7 - 5 \times 8 = 2$

  $7 \times 8 - 6 \times 9 = 2$

  $8 \times 9 - 7 \times 10 = 2$

It looks as if the pattern continues.

Note: Discuss with your class whether or not it is enough to find a few extra lines that fit into the pattern to decide if this is always true.

- Some examples with numbers between 100 and 1,000. Many other calculations are possible.

  $110 \times 111 - 109 \times 112 = 12{,}210 - 12{,}208 = 2$

  $138 \times 139 - 137 \times 140 = 19{,}182 - 19{,}180 = 2$

  $965 \times 966 - 964 \times 967 = 932{,}190 - 932{,}188 = 2$

- In the left picture, there are three parts size n. If you draw them next to one another, you get the second picture but....a part size two is left over!

  The picture on the left shows $(n + 1) \times (n + 2) = n^2 + 3n + 2$.

  The picture on the right shows $n \times (n + 3) = n^2 + 3n$

  Subtracting the two expressions results in 2 which proves the general rule is always true.

You Can Count on It (2)

```
1 × 3 − 0 × 4 = ___
2 × 4 − 1 × 5 = ___
3 × 5 − 2 × 6 = ___
4 × 6 − 3 × 7 = ___
5 × 7 − 4 × 8 = ___

and so on...
```

- What is the regularity in the sequence of calculations?

- Which formula corresponds to this sequence?

- Draw a picture that explains the formula.

Relating patterns in numbers to quadratic expressions

Equivalent quadratic expressions: preformal, formal

- In each column you go up by one. The result is three in each line.

  $1 \times 3 - 0 \times 4 = 3$

  $2 \times 4 - 1 \times 5 = 3$

  $3 \times 5 - 2 \times 6 = 3$

  $4 \times 6 - 3 \times 7 = 3$

  $5 \times 7 - 4 \times 8 = 3$

  The next lines in the sequence are:

  $6 \times 8 - 5 \times 9 = 3$

  $7 \times 9 - 6 \times 10 = 3$

- A formula corresponding to the sequence is: (n starts at zero)

  $(n + 1) \times (n + 3) - n \times (n + 4) = 3$

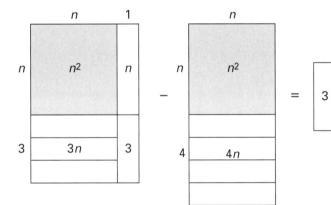

You Can Count on It (3)

• Design a similar sequence of calculations with the same result on each line.

• Write the formula that corresponds with this sequence.

Relating patterns in numbers to quadratic expressions

Equivalent quadratic expressions: preformal, formal

- Answers will vary. One example:

  $2 \times 4 - 0 \times 6 = 8$

  $3 \times 5 - 1 \times 7 = 8$

  $4 \times 6 - 2 \times 8 = 8$

  $5 \times 7 - 3 \times 9 = 8$

  $6 \times 8 - 4 \times 10 = 8$

- A formula that corresponds to the sequence is:

  $(n + 2) \times (n + 4) - n \times (n + 6) = 8$ (n starts at zero).

You Can Count on It (4)

$$(n + 1) \times (n + 2) = n^2 + 3n + 2$$

$$n \times (n + 3) = n^2 + 3n$$

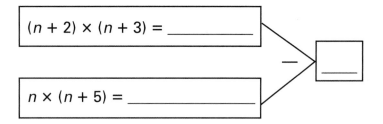

$(n + 2) \times (n + 3) =$ _____

$n \times (n + 5) =$ _____

$-$ [___]

$(n + 2) \times (n + ...) =$ _____

$n \times (n + ...) =$ _____

$-$ [10]

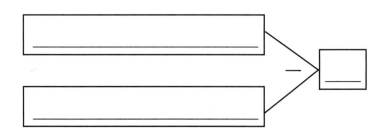

_____

_____

$-$ [___]

Mathematics in Context

Finding equivalent quadratic expressions, using a geometric model: formal

$(n + 2) \times (n + 3) = n^2 + 5n + 6$

$\qquad\qquad\qquad\qquad\qquad - \; 6$

$n \times (n + 5) = n^2 + 5n$

$(n + 2) \times (n + 5) = n^2 + 7n + 10$

$\qquad\qquad\qquad\qquad\qquad - \; 10$

$n \times (n + 7) = n^2 + 7n$

Answers will vary. Have students check their answers with a classmate.

A Remarkable Identity (1)

A rectangular field has a length of 31 m and a width of 29 m.

- Give a quick estimation (in m²) of the area.
- How many square meters does this estimation deviate from the exact area?
- Answer the same two questions for a field of 41 m by 39 m.
- Complete the example below:

51×49 $\Bigg\langle$
  estimation: $50 \times 50 =$ _____
  exact result = _____
$\Bigg]$ deviation = _____

- Make a similar diagram for 61×59.

- Explain using the picture.

The difference between
$n \times n$ and $(n + 1) \times (n - 1)$
is equal to **1**.

or using an equation.

$(n + 1) \times (n - 1) = n^2 - 1$

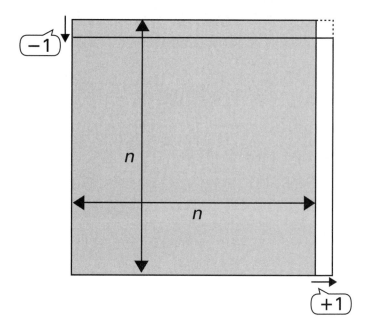

-1

n

n

$+1$

Introduction to the rule
$(a + b)(a - b) = a^2 - b^2$: **informal**

- A quick estimation would be $30 \times 30 = 900$ square meters.

- $31 \times 29 = 899$, so the deviation is only one square meter.

- $40 \times 40 = 1{,}600$

  Exact area: $41 \times 39 = 1{,}599$, again a deviation of one square meter.

  51×49 estimation: $50 \times 50 = 2{,}500$

              exact result is $2{,}499$ deviation is 1

- 61×59 estimation: $60 \times 60 = 3{,}600$

              exact result is $3{,}599$ deviation is 1

- If you "subtract" the two figures representing $n \times n$ and $(n + 1) \times (n - 1)$, the small square in the upper right corner, representing $1 \times 1 = 1$, is left.

  Using the equation $(n + 1)(n - 1) = n^2 - 1$, it is clear that the difference between n^2 and $(n + 1) \times (n - 1)$ is equal to 1.

A Remarkable Identity (2)

- 32 × 28 ⟨ estimation: 30 × 30 = _____ ⟩ deviation = _____
           ⟨ exact result = _____

- Make a similar diagram for 42 × 38.
- Make a diagram for 52 × 48.
- Find a general rule.

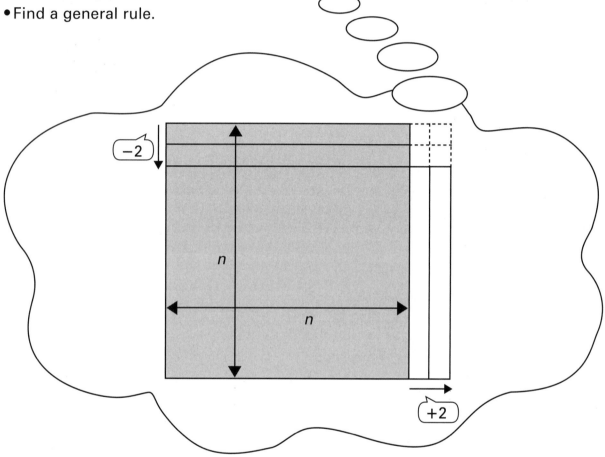

Introduction to the rule
$(a + b)(a - b) = a^2 - b^2$: **preformal**

- 32×28 estimation: $30 \times 30 = 900$
  exact result: $32 \times 28 = 896$ deviation is 4

- 42×38 estimation: $40 \times 40 = 1{,}600$
  exact result: $42 \times 38 = 1{,}596$ deviation is 4

- 52×48 estimation: $50 \times 50 = 2{,}500$
  exact result: $52 \times 48 = 2{,}496$ deviation is 4

- The difference between $n \times n$ and $(n + 2) \times (n - 2)$ is equal to four (2^2); or as an equation:
  $(n + 2) \times (n - 2) = n^2 - 2^2$.

A Remarkable Identity (3)

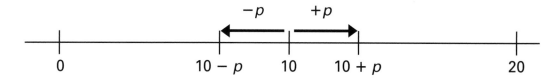

- Use the number line to complete the following.

$(10 + p) + (10 - p) =$ _____

$(10 + p) - (10 - p) =$ _____

August thinks that **10 + p** times **10 − p** is equal to 100.

His reasoning: **10** times **10** is **100**
10 − p is **p** less than **10**,
but **10 + p** is **p** more than **10**,
so they compensate each other.

- Is August right? Explain your reasoning.

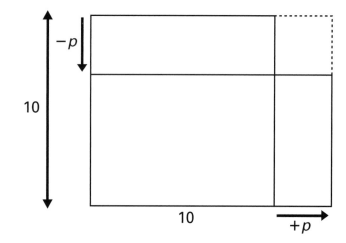

Introduction to the rule

$(a + b)(a - b) = a^2 - b^2$: **preformal**

- $(10 + p) + (10 - p) = 20$

  $(10 + p) - (10 - p) = 2p$

No, August is not right. Look at the picture representing $(10 + p) \times (10 - p)$.

The result is $100 - 10p + 10p - p^2 = 100 - p^2$.

August forgot to subtract the p^2.

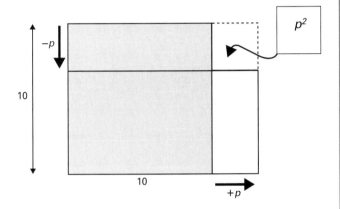

A Remarkable Identity (4)

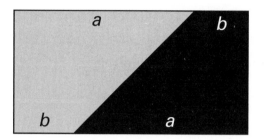

$$a^2 - b^2 = (a + b) \times (a - b)$$

Example:

$$54^2 - 46^2 = (54 + 46) \times (54 - 46) = 100 \times 8 = 800$$

- Calculate in the same way as the example. Do not use a calculator.

$52^2 - 48^2 = $ _____ × _____ = _____

$67^2 - 33^2 = $ _____ × _____. = _____

$501^2 - 499^2 = $ _____ × _____ = _____

- Design some more exercises that can be done in the same style.
- **100** times **100** is more than **100 + p** times **100 − p**.
  How much more?

- n^2 is more than **n + 10** times **n − 10**.
  How much more?

Use of the rule
$(a + b)(a - b) = a^2 - b^2$**: preformal, formal**

- Note: Encourage students who find it difficult to answer the questions to make a drawing.

$52^2 - 48^2 = (52 + 48) \times (52 - 48) =$
$100 \times 4 = 400$

$67^2 - 33^2 = (67 + 33) \times (67 - 33) =$
$100 \times 34 = 3400$

$501^2 - 499^2 = (501 + 499) \times (501 - 499) =$
$1000 \times 2 = 2000$

- Have a classmate check problems and answers.

- 100 times 100 is p^2 more than $100 + p$ times $100 - p$.

Possible explanation:

$100 \times 100 = 10{,}000$

$(100 + p) \times (100 - p) = 100^2 - p^2$
$\qquad\qquad\qquad\qquad\quad = 10{,}000 - p^2$

Note that $(100 + p) \times (100 - p)$ is usually written as $(100 + p)(100 - p)$

- n^2 is 100 more than $n + 10$ times $n - 10$.
Possible explanation:

$(n + 10)(n - 10) = n^2 - 100$

Math Bee

in words	**in symbols**

in words

The sum of *n* and *m* is reduced by **5**.

The sum of *n* and **8** is multiplied by *n*.

The product of *n* and *m* is reduced by *k*.

The square of the sum of *n* and *m*.

The sum of two times *n* and **3** times *k*.

The sum of *n* and **6** is multiplied by
the difference of *n* and **6**.

The product of the third powers of *n* and *m*.

The square of **5** times *n*.

5 times the square of *n*.

in symbols

$$n + m - 5$$

$$(n + 8) \times n$$

Use of symbolic language

$n \times m - k$ or $nm - k$

$(n + m)^2$

$2n + 3k$

$(n + 6) \times (n - 6)$ or $(n + 6)(n - 6)$

$n^3 \times m^3$ or $n^3 m^3$

$(5n)^2$

$5n^2$

The Price of Algebra (1)

Algebra takes time, and time is money.
Here is a detailed "price list."

	Prices:
operations +, −, ×, ÷	1 point each time
squaring	2 points each time
taking to the 3rd power	3 points each time
taking to the 4th power	4 points each time
etc.	etc.
using variables	1 point each time
parentheses and numbers	free

Example 1: What is the price of **3n + m**?

3	**number**	**free**
n	**variable**	**1 point**
3 × n	**multiplication**	**1 point**
m	**variable**	**1 point**
3 × n + m	**addition**	**1 point**
	total price	**4 points**

Example 2: What is the price of $(3n + m)^2$?

3n + m	**just calculated**	**4 points**
(3n + m)^2	**squared**	**2 points**
	total price	**6 points**

- Find the price of each of the following.

n^2 + 3n _____

n(n + 3) _____

(n + 1)(n + 3) _____

n^2 + 4n + 3 _____

A game showing flexibility in working with expressions

Analyzing expressions: formal

$n^2 + 3n$

n	using variable (two times)	2 points
3	number	free
n^2	squaring	2
$3n$	multiplication	1
$n^2 + 3n$	addition	1

_____ +

total   **6 points**

$n(n + 3)$

n	using variable (two times)	2 points
3	number	free
$n + 3$	addition	1
$n(n + 3)$	parentheses	free
$n(n + 3)$	multiplication	1

_____ +

total   **4 points**

$(n + 1)(n + 3)$

n	using variable (two times)	2 points
1, 3	numbers	free
	parentheses	free
$n + 1$	addition	1
$n + 3$	addition	1
$(n + 1)(n + 3)$	multiplication	1

_____ +

total   **5 points**

$n^2 + 4n + 3$

n	using variable (two times)	2 points
4, 3	numbers	free
n^2	squaring	2
$4n$	multiplication	1
$n^2 + 4n + 3$	addition (two times)	2

_____ +

total   **7 points**

The Price of Algebra (2)

$n^2 + 3n$ and $n(n + 3)$ are equivalent expressions.
They do not have the same prices yet! (See page 101.)

- Here are pairs of equivalent expressions.
  For each pair, find out which one is cheaper.

$n + n + n + n$ and $4 \times n$ _____

$n \times n \times n \times n$ and n^4 _____

$n + n + n + n$ and $n + 3n$ _____

$(m + 1)^2$ and $(m + 1)(m + 1)$ _____

$(m + 1)^2$ and $m^2 + 2m + 1$ _____

$a^2 \times a^3$ and a^5 _____

$(a^3)^2$ and a^6 _____

Mathematics in Context

A game showing flexibility in working with powers and expressions
Analyzing expressions: formal

$n + n + n + n$

n	using variable (four times)	4 points
	addition (three times)	3
		+ ————
	total	**7 points**

$4 \times n$

n	using variable	1 point
4	number	free
$4 \times n$	multiplication	1
		+ ————
	total	**2 points**

$4 \times n$ is the cheapest expression.

$n \times n \times n \times n$

n	using variable (four times)	4 points
	multiplication (three times)	3
		+ ————
	total	**7 points**

n^4

n	using variable	1 point
n^4	4th power	4 points
		+ ————
	total	**5 points**

n^4 is the cheapest expression.

$n + n + n + n$ (calculated earlier)	7 points
$n + 3n$	4 points

$n + 3n$ is the cheapest expression.

$(m + 1)^2$	4 points
$(m + 1)(m + 1)$	5 points

$(m + 1)^2$ is the cheapest expression.

$(m + 1)^2$	4 points
$m^2 + 2m + 1$	7 points

$(m + 1)^2$ is the cheapest expression.

$a^2 \times a^3$	8 points
a^5	6 points

a^5 is the cheapest expression.

$(a^3)^2$	6 points
a^6	7 points

$(a^3)^2$ is the cheapest expression.

The Price of Algebra (3)

- Compare the prices of a^4b^4 and $(a^2b^2)^2$.

  Both expressions are equivalent, but the second one is 2 points cheaper.

- Try to find an expression as cheap as possible, that is equivalent to a^4b^4.

You can rewrite n^{15} in different ways by using equivalent expressions.

Here are some possibilities.

$n \times n \times n \times n \times n \times n \times n \times n \times n \times n \times n \times n \times n \times n \times n$

$(n \times n \times n \times n \times n)^3$

$n^{10} \times n^5$

- Which of them is cheaper than n^{15}?

  Try to find an equivalent expression with the lowest price.

- Find the cheapest expression equivalent to x^{24}.

A game showing flexibility in working with powers: formal

- $a^4 b^4$ 11 points
  $(a^2 b^2)^2$ 9 points

- An equivalent expression that is as cheap as possible is $(ab)^4$, or $((ab)^2)^2$, which costs 7 points.

- n^{15} costs 16 points.

  $n \times n \times n \times n \times n \times n \times n \times n \times$
  $n \times n \times n \times n \times n \times n \times n$ 29 points

  $(n \times n \times n \times n \times n)^3$ 12 points, **cheaper than n^{15}**

  $n^{10} \times n^5$ 18 points

  The two equivalent expressions that are as cheap as possible are $(n^3)^5$, which costs 9 points each, or $(n^5)^3$.

- An equivalent expression of x^{24} that is as cheap as possible is $((x^4)^2)^3$, which costs 10 points.

Splitting Fractions (1)

Four thousand years ago, mathematicians in Egypt worked with **unit fractions**, such as:

$$\frac{1}{2}, \frac{1}{3}, \frac{1}{4}, \frac{1}{5}, \text{ etc.}$$

All of these fractions have a **numerator** of **1**.

A fraction with a numerator different from **1**, can be split up into unit fractions.

Example 1:

$$\frac{3}{4} = \frac{1}{4} + \frac{1}{4} + \frac{1}{4}$$

Splitting into unit fractions becomes less obvious if you want to use as few unit fractions as possible, in this case:

$$\frac{3}{4} = \frac{2+1}{4} = \frac{1}{2} + \frac{1}{4}$$

Example 2:

$$\frac{19}{24} = \frac{12+6+1}{24} = \frac{1}{2} + \frac{1}{4} + \frac{1}{24}$$

• Try to split up into unit fractions, using as few fractions as possible.

$$\frac{7}{8} = \frac{\boxed{} + \boxed{} + \boxed{}}{8} = \frac{1}{\boxed{}} + \frac{1}{\boxed{}} + \frac{1}{\boxed{}}$$

$$\frac{5}{6} = \boxed{} = \boxed{}$$

$$\frac{13}{16} = \boxed{} = \boxed{}$$

$$\frac{13}{18} = \boxed{} = \boxed{}$$

$$\frac{99}{100} = \boxed{} = \boxed{}$$

**Introduction to working with fractions
containing variables: informal**

Simplifying fractions

Historic link.

$$\frac{7}{8} = \frac{\boxed{4} + \boxed{2} + \boxed{1}}{8} = \frac{1}{\boxed{2}} + \frac{1}{\boxed{4}} + \frac{1}{\boxed{8}}$$

$$\frac{5}{6} = \boxed{\frac{3+2}{6}} = \boxed{\frac{1}{2} + \frac{1}{3}}$$

$$\frac{13}{16} = \boxed{\frac{8+4+1}{16}} = \boxed{\frac{1}{2} + \frac{1}{4} + \frac{1}{16}}$$

$$\frac{13}{18} = \boxed{\frac{9+2+2}{18}} = \boxed{\frac{1}{2} + \frac{1}{9} + \frac{1}{9}} \quad \text{or}$$

$$\boxed{\frac{6+6+1}{18}} = \boxed{\frac{1}{3} + \frac{1}{3} + \frac{1}{18}}$$

However, the unit fractions should have different
denominators, so:

$$\frac{13}{18} = \boxed{\frac{9+3+1}{18}} = \boxed{\frac{1}{2} + \frac{1}{6} + \frac{1}{18}}$$

One possible solution:

$$\frac{99}{100} = \boxed{\frac{50+25+20+4}{100}} = \boxed{\frac{1}{2} + \frac{1}{4} + \frac{1}{5} + \frac{1}{25}}$$

Splitting Fractions (2)

If the numerator and denominator of a fraction are divided (or multiplied) by the same number, the value of the fraction does not change.

Example 1:

$\dfrac{5}{15} = \dfrac{1}{3}$ (The numerator and denominator are divided by 3.)

$\dfrac{b}{5b} = \dfrac{1}{5}$ (The numerator and denominator are divided by **b**.)

The rule is used to split fractions into unit fractions.

Examples:

$$\frac{n+1}{3n} = \frac{n}{3n} + \frac{1}{3n} = \frac{1}{3} + \frac{1}{3n}$$

$$\frac{a+b}{ab} = \frac{a}{ab} + \frac{b}{ab} = \frac{1}{b} + \frac{1}{a}$$

• Split each fraction into as few unit fractions as possible.

$\dfrac{p+5}{5p} = \boxed{}$ $\qquad$ $\dfrac{p+3}{3pq} = \boxed{}$

$\dfrac{x+y}{xy} = \boxed{}$ $\qquad$ $\dfrac{k+m+n}{kmn} = \boxed{}$

• Complete each expression.

$\dfrac{\boxed{} + \boxed{}}{ab} = \dfrac{1}{a} + \dfrac{1}{b}$

$\dfrac{\boxed{} + \boxed{} + \boxed{}}{abc} = \dfrac{1}{a} + \dfrac{1}{b} + \dfrac{1}{c}$

$\dfrac{\boxed{} + \boxed{} + \boxed{} + \boxed{}}{abcd} = \dfrac{1}{a} + \dfrac{1}{b} + \dfrac{1}{c} + \dfrac{1}{d}$

Working with fractions containing variables: preformal

Simplifying fractions

- $\dfrac{p+5}{5p}$ = $\boxed{\dfrac{p}{5p} + \dfrac{5}{5p} = \dfrac{1}{5} + \dfrac{1}{p}}$

  $\dfrac{x+y}{xy}$ = $\boxed{\dfrac{x}{xy} + \dfrac{y}{xy} = \dfrac{1}{y} + \dfrac{1}{x}}$

  $\dfrac{p+3}{3pq}$ = $\boxed{\dfrac{p}{3pq} + \dfrac{3}{3pq} = \dfrac{1}{3q} + \dfrac{1}{pq}}$

  $\dfrac{k+m+n}{kmn}$ = $\boxed{\dfrac{k}{kmn} + \dfrac{m}{kmn} + \dfrac{n}{kmn} = \dfrac{1}{mn} + \dfrac{1}{kn} + \dfrac{1}{km}}$

- $\dfrac{\boxed{b} + \boxed{a}}{ab}$ = $\boxed{\dfrac{b}{ab} + \dfrac{a}{ab}} = \dfrac{1}{a} + \dfrac{1}{b}$

  $\dfrac{\boxed{bc} + \boxed{ac} + \boxed{ab}}{abc}$ = $\boxed{\dfrac{bc}{abc} + \dfrac{ac}{abc} + \dfrac{ab}{abc}} = \dfrac{1}{a} + \dfrac{1}{b} + \dfrac{1}{c}$

  $\dfrac{\boxed{bcd} + \boxed{acd} + \boxed{abd} + \boxed{abc}}{abcd}$ = $\dfrac{1}{a} + \dfrac{1}{b} + \dfrac{1}{c} + \dfrac{1}{d}$

Fractions on Strips (1)

- Find the missing numbers and expressions. In each case,
  n starts at 1.

First problem (subtraction):

Strip 1 (top to bottom): 1, $\frac{1}{2}$, $\frac{1}{3}$, $\frac{1}{4}$, $\frac{1}{5}$, □, □

$-$

Strip 2: $\frac{1}{2}$, $\frac{1}{3}$, $\frac{1}{4}$, $\frac{1}{5}$, $\frac{1}{6}$, □, □

$=$

Strip 3: $\frac{1}{2}$, $\frac{1}{6}$, $\frac{1}{12}$, $\frac{1}{20}$, $\frac{1}{30}$, □, □

$$\frac{1}{n} - \frac{1}{n+1} = \boxed{}$$

Second problem (addition):

Strip 1 (top to bottom): 1, $\frac{1}{2}$, $\frac{1}{3}$, $\frac{1}{4}$, $\frac{1}{5}$, □, □

$+$

Strip 2: $\frac{1}{2}$, $\frac{1}{3}$, $\frac{1}{4}$, $\frac{1}{5}$, $\frac{1}{6}$, □, □

$=$

Strip 3: $\frac{3}{2}$, $\frac{5}{6}$, $\frac{7}{12}$, $\frac{9}{20}$, $\frac{11}{30}$, □, □

$$\frac{1}{n} + \frac{1}{n+1} = \boxed{}$$

Reducing, adding, and subtracting simple rational expressions: preformal

Have students check whether the numbers on their strips fit the expressions.

$$\frac{1}{n} - \frac{1}{n+1} = \frac{1}{n(n+1)}$$

$$\frac{1}{n} + \frac{1}{n+1} = \frac{2n+1}{n(n+1)}$$

Fractions on Strips (2)

- Find the missing numbers and expressions. In each case, n starts at 1.

First set (multiplication):

Strip 1: 1, $\frac{1}{2}$, $\frac{1}{3}$, $\frac{1}{4}$, $\frac{1}{5}$, (blank), (blank)

$\times$

Strip 2: $\frac{1}{2}$, $\frac{1}{3}$, $\frac{1}{4}$, $\frac{1}{5}$, $\frac{1}{6}$, (blank), (blank)

$=$

Strip 3: $\frac{1}{2}$, $\frac{1}{6}$, $\frac{1}{12}$, $\frac{1}{20}$, $\frac{1}{30}$, (blank), (blank)

$$\frac{1}{n} \times \frac{1}{n+1} = \boxed{}$$

Second set (division):

Strip 1: 1, $\frac{1}{2}$, $\frac{1}{3}$, $\frac{1}{4}$, $\frac{1}{5}$, (blank), (blank)

$\div$

Strip 2: $\frac{1}{2}$, $\frac{1}{3}$, $\frac{1}{4}$, $\frac{1}{5}$, $\frac{1}{6}$, (blank), (blank)

$=$

Strip 3: 2, $\frac{3}{2}$, $\frac{4}{3}$, $\frac{5}{4}$, $\frac{6}{5}$, (blank), (blank)

$$\frac{1}{n} \div \frac{1}{n+1} = \boxed{}$$

Reducing, multiplying, and dividing simple rational expressions: preformal

Have students check whether the numbers on their strips fit the expressions.

$$\frac{1}{n} \times \frac{1}{n+1} = \frac{1}{n(n+1)}$$

$$\frac{1}{n} \div \frac{1}{n+1} = \frac{n+1}{n}$$

Multiplying Fractions (1)

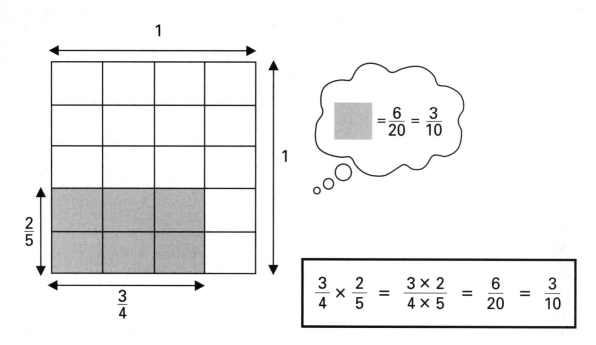

$$\frac{3}{4} \times \frac{2}{5} = \frac{3 \times 2}{4 \times 5} = \frac{6}{20} = \frac{3}{10}$$

- Draw a picture to show that

$$\frac{4}{5} \times \frac{2}{3} = \frac{4 \times 2}{5 \times 3} = \frac{8}{15}.$$

- Calculate

$\frac{3}{5} \times \frac{1}{4} =$ [ ] $\frac{3}{5} \times \frac{4}{5} =$ [ ]

$\frac{3}{4} \times \frac{1}{5} =$ [ ] $\frac{1}{5} \times \frac{1}{4} =$ [ ]

- Calculate $p^2 + q^2 + 2pq$ for $p = \frac{1}{3}$ and $q = \frac{2}{3}$.

- Also for $p = \frac{2}{5}$ and $q = \frac{3}{5}$.

- Calculate $p^2 - q^2$ for $p = \frac{3}{4}$ and $q = \frac{1}{4}$.

- Also for $p = \frac{5}{8}$ and $q = \frac{3}{8}$.

Multiplying Fractions (1)

Multiplication of fractions, with and without variables

- $\frac{4}{5} \times \frac{2}{3} = \frac{8}{15}$

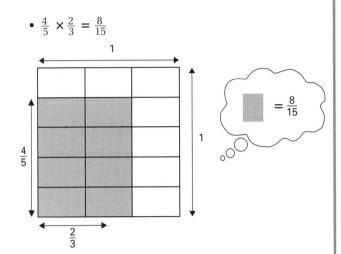

$$\boxed{} = \frac{8}{15}$$

Drawing a picture may help to solve the next problem. Note that fractions in the answer should always be simplified as far as possible.

- $\frac{3}{5} \times \frac{1}{4} = \frac{3 \times 1}{5 \times 4} = \frac{3}{20}$ $\frac{3}{5} \times \frac{4}{5} = \frac{3 \times 4}{5 \times 5} = \frac{12}{25}$

  $\frac{3}{4} \times \frac{1}{5} = \frac{3 \times 1}{4 \times 5} = \frac{3}{20}$ $\frac{1}{5} \times \frac{1}{4} = \frac{1 \times 1}{5 \times 4} = \frac{1}{20}$

- $(\frac{1}{3})^2 + (\frac{2}{3})^2 + 2 \times \frac{1}{3} \times \frac{2}{3} = \frac{1}{9} + \frac{4}{9} + \frac{4}{9} = \frac{9}{9} = 1$

- $(\frac{2}{5})^2 + (\frac{3}{5})^2 + 2 \times \frac{2}{5} \times \frac{3}{5} = \frac{4}{25} + \frac{9}{25} + \frac{12}{25} = \frac{25}{25} = 1$

Note: Some students may realize that, since $\frac{1}{3} + \frac{2}{3} = 1$ and $1^2 = 1$ and for the next problem: $\frac{2}{5} + \frac{3}{5} = 1$ and $1^2 = 1$ there should be an easier way to solve the problem! They may remember to use $p^2 + q^2 + 2pq = (p + q)^2$, which makes the problem much easier. It is a way to show the power of using algebra!

- $(\frac{3}{4})^2 - (\frac{1}{4})^2 = \frac{9}{16} - \frac{1}{16} = \frac{8}{16} = \frac{1}{2}$

- $(\frac{5}{8})^2 - (\frac{3}{8})^2 = \frac{25}{64} - \frac{9}{64} = \frac{16}{64} = \frac{1}{4}$

Some students may remember that $p^2 - q^2 = (p - q)(p + q)$ which makes the problem easier.

$(\frac{3}{4} - \frac{1}{4})(\frac{3}{4} + \frac{1}{4}) = \frac{1}{2}$ And for the next problem:

$(\frac{5}{8} - \frac{3}{8})(\frac{5}{8} + \frac{3}{8}) = \frac{1}{4}$

Multiplying Fractions (2)

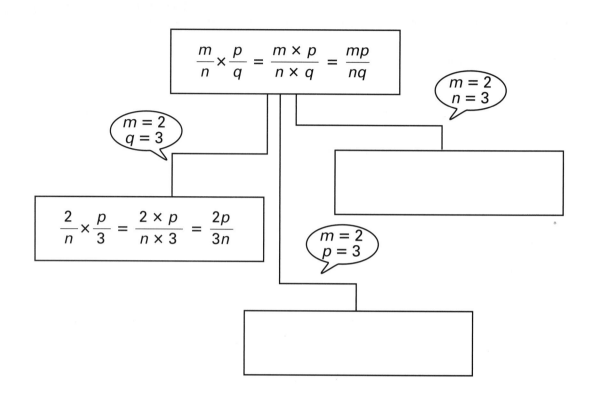

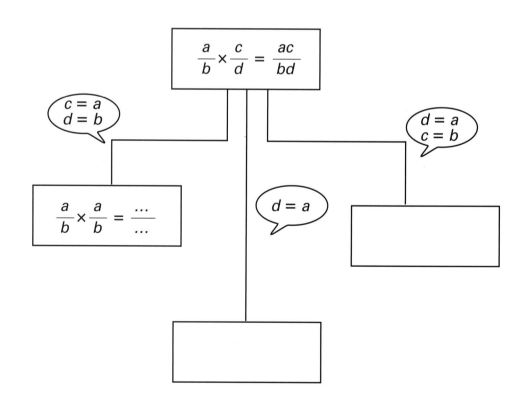

Multiplying Fractions (2)

Multiplication of fractions with variables: formal

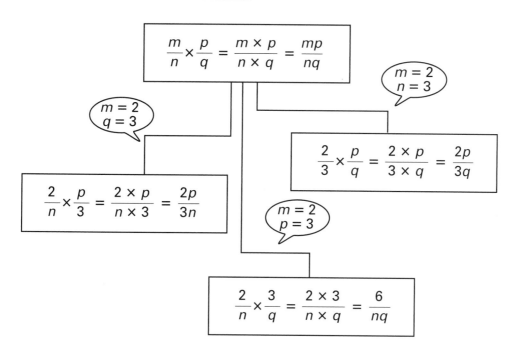

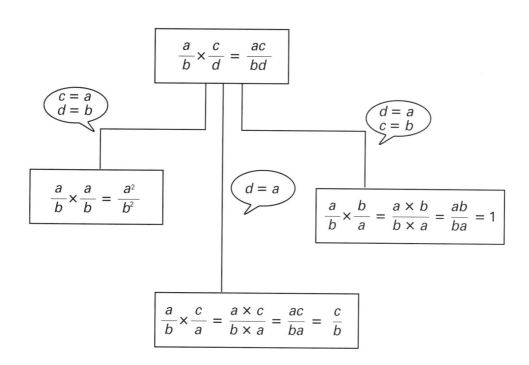

Intermediate Fractions (1)

You have seen that:

$$\frac{m}{n} \times \frac{p}{q} = \frac{m \times p}{n \times q} \qquad \text{(A).}$$

Maybe you think that addition follows a similar rule.

$$\frac{m}{n} + \frac{p}{q} \overset{?}{=} \frac{m+p}{n+q} \qquad \text{(B).}$$

- In the same way, calculate the "sum" of $\frac{3}{5}$ and $\frac{1}{4}$.

Check to see whether the result is somewhere *between* $\frac{3}{5}$ and $\frac{1}{4}$.

So it cannot be the real sum of both fractions!

- How can you calculate the sum of $\frac{3}{5}$ and $\frac{1}{4}$?

Formula (B) is not a good recipe to add fractions, but it is a recipe to find intermediate fractions.

- Check for some examples to see if the value of $\frac{m}{n} + \frac{p}{q}$ always lies between the values of $\frac{m}{n}$ and $\frac{p}{q}$.

- Design some examples, for which the value of $\frac{m}{n} + \frac{p}{q}$ is in the middle between the values of $\frac{m}{n}$ and $\frac{p}{q}$.

In a group of 31 students, there are more girls than boys (19 versus 12).
In a parallel group (29 students), it is just the reverse (12 versus 17).
During physical education, girls and boys of both groups are in separate classes, one all girls class (19 + 12) and one all boys class (12 + 17).

- Check to see if this results in a more balanced distribution of girls and boys.

- What does this example have to do with the concept of intermediate fractions?

"Pseudo-addition" of fractions, with and without variables

- $\frac{3}{5} + \frac{1}{4} \overset{?}{=} \frac{4}{9}$

  To check that this result is between $\frac{3}{5}$ and $\frac{1}{4}$ so the addition cannot be correct, students may use a calculator.

- In order to find the correct answer, you will need to find a common denominator for both fractions, which is $5 \times 4 = 20$.

  $\frac{3}{5} + \frac{1}{4} = \frac{12}{20} + \frac{5}{20} = \frac{17}{20}$

- Some examples to show that $\frac{m+p}{n+q}$ lies between $\frac{m}{n}$ and $\frac{p}{q}$:

  $\frac{m}{n} = \frac{5}{8}; \frac{p}{q} = \frac{4}{10}$ $\frac{m+p}{n+q} = \frac{5+4}{8+10} = \frac{9}{18} = \frac{1}{2}$.

  Students may want to draw a number line to show $\frac{1}{2}$ is between $\frac{5}{8}$ and $\frac{4}{10}$

  The second example, $\frac{m}{n} = \frac{5}{8}; \frac{p}{q} = \frac{2}{5}$, results in $\frac{m+p}{n+q} = \frac{5+2}{8+5} = \frac{7}{13}$.

  This is interesting because since $\frac{4}{10} = \frac{2}{5}$, adding the two fractions should give the same result! However, $\frac{7}{13} \neq \frac{1}{2}$; it is between $\frac{5}{8}$ and $\frac{2}{5}$.

- An example to show that $\frac{m+p}{n+q}$ can be in the middle between $\frac{m}{n}$ and $\frac{p}{q}$:

  $\frac{m}{n} = \frac{3}{4}; \frac{p}{q} = \frac{1}{4} = \frac{m+p}{n+q} = \frac{3+1}{4+4} = \frac{4}{8} = \frac{1}{2}$, since $\frac{1}{2} = \frac{2}{4}$, this is in the middle between $\frac{3}{4}$ and $\frac{1}{4}$.

  Note: In general $\frac{a}{n}; \frac{b}{n}; \frac{a+b}{2n} = \frac{1}{2}(\frac{a}{n} + \frac{b}{n})$

- In the girls' class, there are $19 + 12 = 31$ students. In the boys' class, there are $12 + 17 = 29$ students. The ratio girls versus boys is now $\frac{19+12}{12+17} = \frac{31}{29}$, which is more balanced than $\frac{19}{12}$ or $\frac{12}{17}$ in the original groups.

- $\frac{19+12}{12+17} = \frac{31}{29}$ is an intermediate fraction between $\frac{19}{12}$ and $\frac{12}{17}$.

Intermediate Fractions (2)

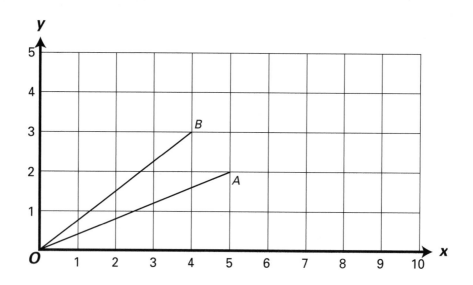

- What fraction represents the slope of the line *OA*?

- What fraction represents the slope of the line *OB*?

- Add the numerators and denominators of both fractions.
  Which fraction do you get?

- Draw a line starting at *O*, with a slope equal to this fraction.
  How can you see whether this fraction is an intermediate
  fraction of the fractions corresponding to the slopes of
  OA and *OB*?

- Do the same with two other lines starting at *O*.
  Determine the corresponding fractions, add the numerators
  and denominators to get a new fraction, and draw the line
  whose slope is equal to the new fraction.

"Pseudo-addition" of fractions
Relation to slope

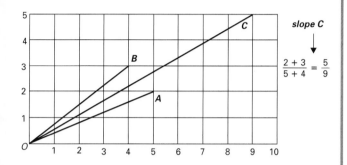

slope C

↓

$$\frac{2+3}{5+4} = \frac{5}{9}$$

- slope of line OA: $\frac{2}{5}$

- slope of line OB: $\frac{3}{4}$

- Adding the numerators and denominators of both fractions results in $\frac{5}{9}$.

- You can see that $\frac{5}{9}$ is an intermediate fraction between $\frac{2}{3}$ and $\frac{3}{4}$ because the new line is an intermediate line between lines OA and OB.

- Students' own examples will vary. Have students check each other's examples.

Intermediate Fractions (3)

New fractions can be made step by step using the recipe
to make intermediate fractions.

• Fill the empty cells in the "tree" below.

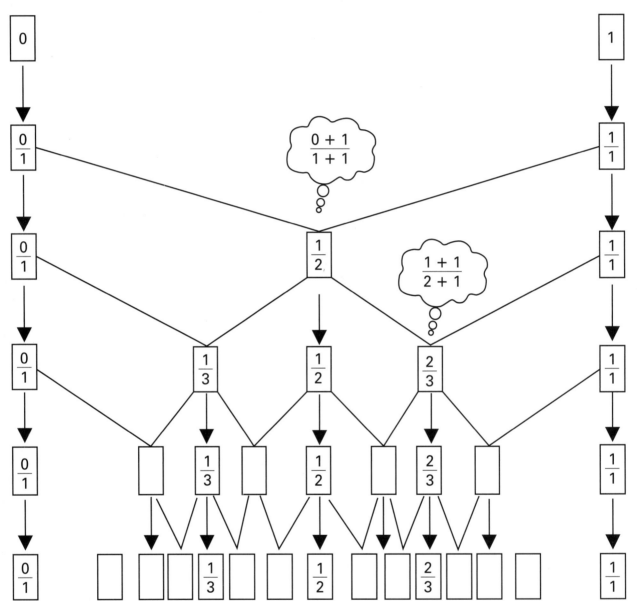

"Pseudo-addition" of fractions

Fractions that fill the empty cells:

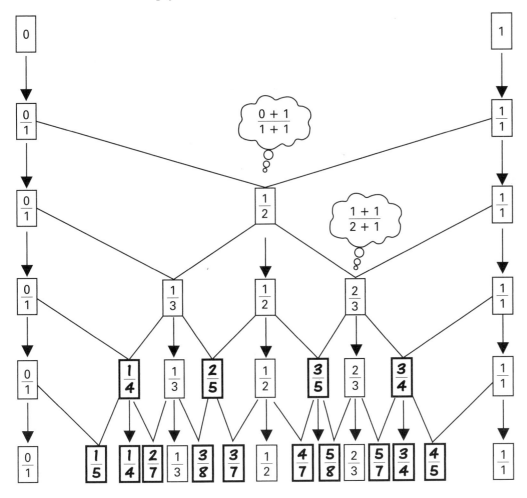

Adding Fractions

The correct formula for adding fractions is (unfortunately) much more complicated than the rule for making intermediate fractions.

Here it is. $\dfrac{m}{n} + \dfrac{p}{q} = \dfrac{m \times q \ + \ n \times p}{n \times q}$

- Check this formula for the fractions $\dfrac{3}{5}$ and $\dfrac{1}{4}$.

- Design some more examples to check the addition formula.

- What (simpler) formula do you get if $m = 1$ and $p = 1$?

- What (obvious) formula do you get if $n = 1$ and $q = 1$?

The addition formula is more complicated than necessary in many cases, but it's always correct.

Here is an example, in which you can add fractions without any formula.

$$\frac{3}{n} + \frac{2}{n} = \frac{5}{n}$$

- If you use the addition formula (with $m = 3$, $p = 2$, and $q = n$), you would find $\dfrac{3}{n} + \dfrac{2}{n} = \dfrac{3 \times n \ + \ n \times 2}{n \times n}$.

  Show that the result is equal to $\dfrac{5}{n}$.

- Find one fraction equal to $\dfrac{m}{3} + \dfrac{m}{2}$.

- Do the same thing for $\dfrac{m}{3} + \dfrac{p}{2}$.

Mathematics in Context

Addition of fractions, also with variables: formal

- $\frac{m}{n} = \frac{3}{5}$ and $\frac{p}{q} = \frac{1}{4}$ $\frac{3}{5} + \frac{1}{4} = \frac{3 \times 4 + 5 \times 1}{5 \times 4} = \frac{12 + 5}{20} = \frac{17}{20}$

- Students examples will vary. Have classmates check each other's examples.

- $m = 1$ and $p = 1$ changes the formula into
  $\frac{1}{n} + \frac{1}{q} = \frac{q + n}{n \times q}$

- $n = 1$ and $q = 1$ changes the formula into
  $\frac{m}{1} + \frac{p}{1} = \frac{m + p}{1}$

- $\frac{3 \times n + n \times 2}{n \times n} = \frac{5n}{n \times n} = \frac{5}{n}$

- $\frac{m}{3} + \frac{m}{2} = \frac{2m}{6} + \frac{3m}{6} = \frac{5m}{6}$

- $\frac{m}{3} + \frac{p}{2} = \frac{2m}{6} + \frac{3p}{6} = \frac{2m + 3p}{6}$

Trees with Fractions (1)

- Fill in the missing expressions.

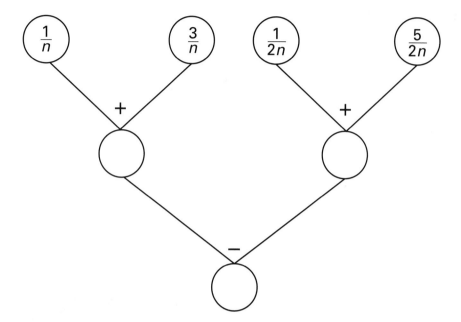

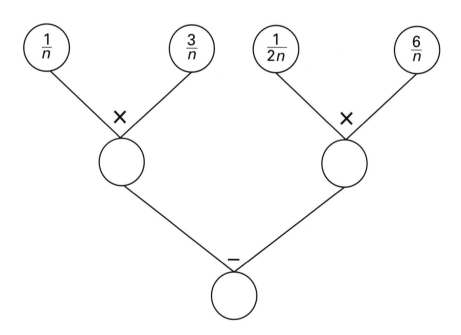

Formal addition and subtraction with fractions

Using variables

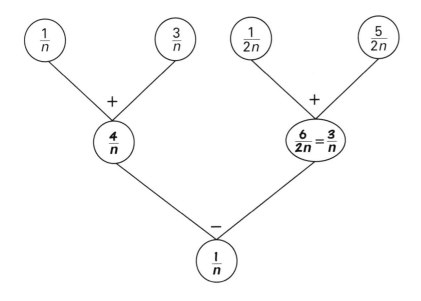

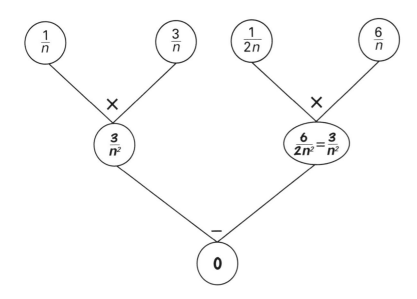

Trees with Fractions (2)

• Fill in the missing expressions.

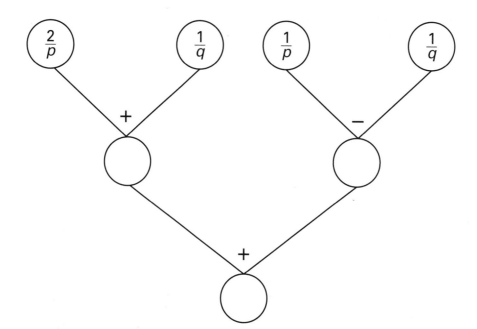

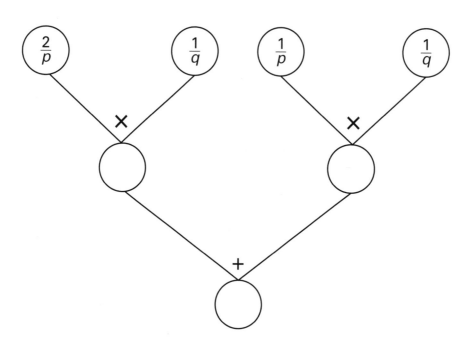

Addition, subtraction, and multiplication with
fractions using variables: formal

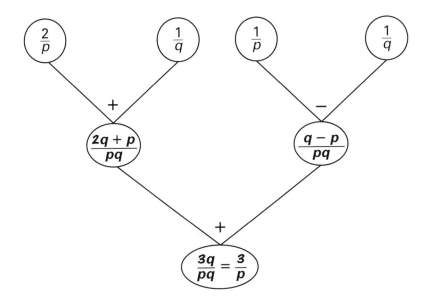

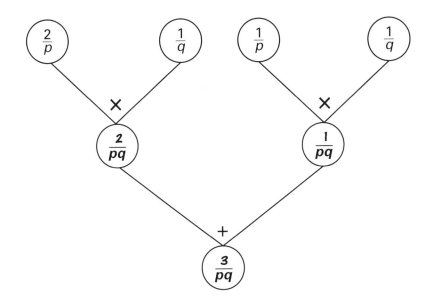

More Fractions

$$\frac{a}{2} + \frac{a}{3} + \frac{a}{6} = \boxed{}$$

$$\frac{2}{a} + \frac{3}{a} + \frac{6}{a} = \boxed{}$$

$$\frac{b}{2} + \frac{b}{4} + \frac{b}{6} + \frac{b}{12} = \boxed{}$$

$$\frac{2}{b} + \frac{4}{b} + \frac{6}{b} + \frac{12}{b} = \boxed{}$$

$$\frac{c}{2} + \frac{c}{6} + \frac{c}{10} + \frac{c}{12} + \frac{c}{15} + \frac{c}{60} = \boxed{}$$

$$\frac{2}{c} + \frac{6}{c} + \frac{10}{c} + \frac{12}{c} + \frac{15}{c} + \frac{60}{c} = \boxed{}$$

- Design one pair of additions in the same style.

Addition of fractions using variables: formal

$\frac{3a}{6} + \frac{2a}{6} + \frac{a}{6} = \frac{6a}{6}$ or a

$\frac{2}{a} + \frac{3}{a} + \frac{6}{a} = \frac{11}{a}$

$\frac{6b}{12} + \frac{3b}{12} + \frac{2b}{12} + \frac{b}{12} = \frac{12b}{12}$ or b

$\frac{2}{b} + \frac{4}{b} + \frac{6}{b} + \frac{12}{b} = \frac{24}{b}$

$\frac{30c}{60} + \frac{10c}{60} + \frac{6c}{60} + \frac{5c}{60} + \frac{4c}{60} + \frac{c}{60} = \frac{56c}{60}$

$\frac{2}{c} + \frac{6}{c} + \frac{10}{c} + \frac{12}{c} + \frac{15}{c} + \frac{60}{c} = \frac{105}{c}$

Students' own designs of pairs of additions will vary. Have classmates check each other's solutions.

Equations with Squares (1)

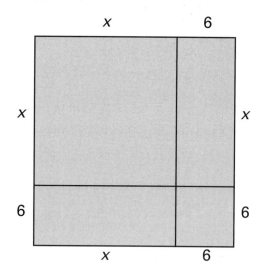

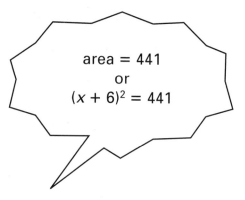

area = 441
or
$(x + 6)^2 = 441$

- Calculate the value of x.

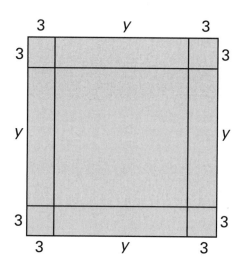

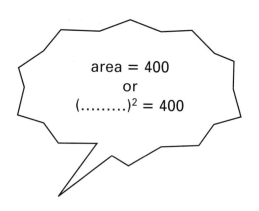

area = 400
or
$(\ldots\ldots)^2 = 400$

- Calculate the value of y.

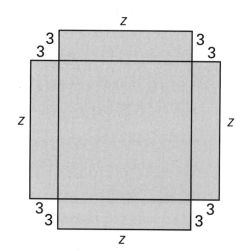

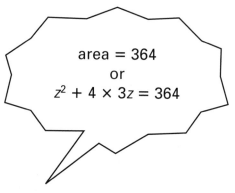

area = 364
or
$z^2 + 4 \times 3z = 364$

- Calculate the value of z.

Equations with Squares (1)

Solving quadratic equations where variables are positive whole numbers: preformal

Equivalent equations

Geometric algebra.

- The area of the square is 441, so the length of one side is 21 since $21 \times 21 = 441$.

  The length of one side can also be expressed as $x + 6$.

  $x + 6 = 21$

  $x = 15$

- The area of the square can be expressed as $3 + y + 3$ or $6 + y$.

  $(6 + y)^2 = 400$

  $400 = 20^2$

  $6 + y = 20$

  $y = 14$

- If you "fill up" the small squares of 3×3, a whole square is made with area

  $364 + 4 \times 9 = 400$.

  $400 = 20^2$, so the length of one side of this square is 20.

  The length of one side of the square can be expressed as $3 + z + 3$ or $6 + z$.

  $6 + z = 20$

  $z = 14$

  Students should notice that the third representation equals the previous one except for the four small squares which each have an area of 9. The new area is $400 - 4 \times 9 = 364$ and $z = y$.

  $(z + 6)^2 = 400$ and $z^2 + 4 \times 3z = 364$ are equivalent equations; they have the same solution.

  Some students may remember that $(z + 6)^2$ can be rewritten as $z^2 + 12z + 36$.

  $z^2 + 12z + 36 = 400$ is equivalent to $z^2 + 12z = 400 - 36 = 364$.

Equations with Squares (2)

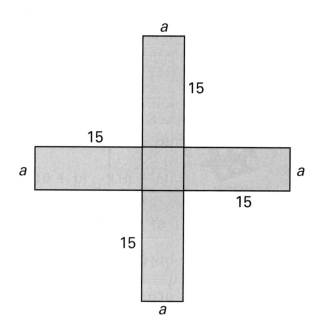

a

15

15

a   a

15

15

a

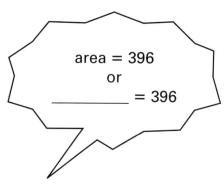

area = 396
or
_____ = 396

● Calculate the value of *a*.

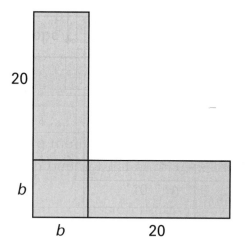

20

b

b   20

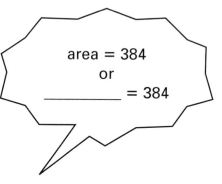

area = 384
or
_____ = 384

● Calculate the value of *b*.

Solving quadratic equations where variables are positive whole numbers: preformal

Equivalent equations

Geometric algebra

- The area of the shaded part can be expressed as $a^2 + 4 \times 15a$.

  The equation to be solved is $a^2 + 4 \times 15a = 396$.

  If you "fill up" the squares of 15×15, a whole square is made with area

  $396 + 4 \times 15^2 = 396 + 4 \times 225 = 1{,}296$.

  $1{,}296 = 36^2$, so the length of one side of this square is 36.

  The length of one side of the square can be expressed as $15 + a + 15$ or $30 + a$.

  $30 + a = 36$

  $a = 6$

  $(30 + a)^2 = 1{,}296$ and $a^2 + 4 \times 15a = 396$ are equivalent equations.

- The area of the shaded part can be expressed as $20b + b^2 + 20b$ or $b^2 + 40b$.

  The equation to be solved is $b^2 + 40b = 384$.

  If you "fill up" the square of 20×20, a whole square is made with an area of

  $384 + 400 = 784$.

  $784 = 28^2$, so the length of one side of this square is 28.

  The length of one side of the square can be expressed as $b + 20$.

  $b + 20 = 28$

  $b = 8$

  $b^2 + 40b = 384$ and $(b + 20)^2 = 784$ are equivalent equations.

Equations with Squares (3)

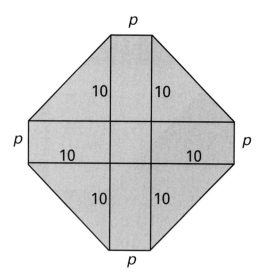

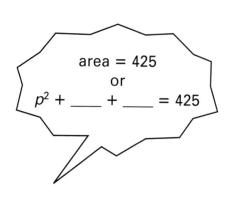

area = 425
or
$p^2 +$ ____ + ____ = 425

- Calculate the value of **p**.

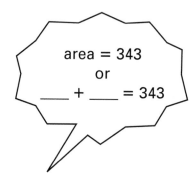

area = 343
or
____ + ____ = 343

- Calculate the value of *x*.

x

x 42

Solving quadratic equations where variables are positive whole numbers: preformal

Equivalent equations

Geometric algebra

- The equation to be solved is
  $p^2 + 4 \times 10 \times p + 4 \times \frac{1}{2} \times 10 \times 10 = 425$ or
  $p^2 + 40p + 200 = 425$.
  You can "fill up" the figure with four halves of squares, total area $4 \times 50 = 200$.
  A new square is created, area $425 + 200 = 625$.
  $625 = 25^2$, so one side of this new square is 25.
  The side of the square can be expressed as
  $10 + p + 10$ or $p + 20$.
  $p + 20 = 25$
  $p = 5$
  $p^2 + 40p + 200 = 425$ and $(p + 20)^2 = 625$ are equivalent equations.

- $x^2 + 42x = 343$
  $x^2 + 21x + 21x + 441 = 343 + 441$
  $(x + 21)^2 = 784 = 28^2$
  $x + 21 = 28$
  $x = 7$

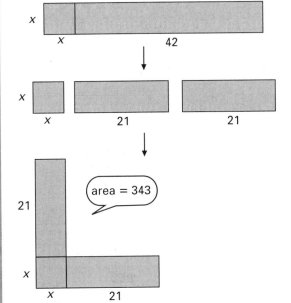

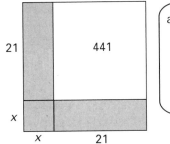

area = 343

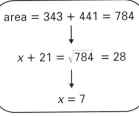

area = 343 + 441 = 784

$x + 21 = \sqrt{784} = 28$

$x = 7$

Babylonian Algebra (1)

About 1700 B.C., the Babylonians could solve many algebraic problems.

One type of problem was to calculate two numbers given the sum and the product of those numbers.

Here is an example:

- Find two numbers such that their sum is 18, and the product is 65.

  Solve this problem by trial and error.

You can probably solve this problem rather quickly.

- Find two numbers such that their sum is 180, and the product is 6,500.

- Find two numbers such that their sum is 180, and the product is 7,700.

The next problem is more difficult. (Use your calculator.)

- Find two numbers such that their sum is 180, and the product is 7,776.

Solving quadratic equations: informal

Historic link

- The numbers, found by using a trial and error method, are 5 and 13.

- Have students check the answers by adding and multiplying the numbers they found.

- The numbers are 50 and 130.

- In the previous problem, you found 50 + 130 = 180 and 50 × 130 = 6,500.

  Now you need to find a larger product, for instance 60 × 120 = 7,200, which is not enough.

  70 × 110 = 7,700 and 70 + 110 = 180.

  The numbers are 70 and 110.

- The product 7,776 is near 7,700, so look for numbers in a smart way.

  75 × 105 = 7,875, too much, and the product ends at 6, so the numbers cannot end at 5.

  74 × 106 = 7,844, too much, and 4 × 6 does not end at 6.

  72 × 108 = 7,776

  The numbers are 72 and 108.

Babylonian Algebra (2)

The Babylonians didn't use a method of trial and error but discovered an algebraic solution.

They reasoned more or less like this.

Suppose the sum of two numbers is 180, and the product is 7,776.

If the numbers were equal, each of them should be 90.

But 90 × 90 = 8,100, and this is larger than 7,776.

So one of the numbers must be larger than 90, say 90 + *d*,

and the other one must be **equally** smaller, therefore 90 − *d*.

The product of 90 + *d* and 90 − *d* is equal to 8,100 − *d²*.

- Explain this from the diagram below.

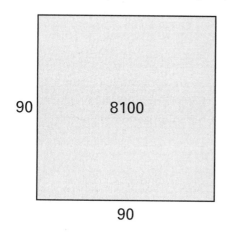
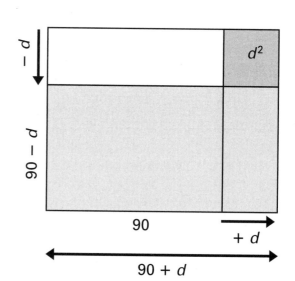

The Babylonians continued.

On the other hand we know that the product must be 7,776, so

$$8100 - d^2 = 7{,}776$$

- Now calculate the value of **d**.

- What are the two numbers?

Solving quadratic equations: informal

Historic link

- From the sides of a 90 by 90 square, subtract a length of d from one side and add a length of d to the other side.

  The area of the rectangle with sides $90 + d$ and $90 - d$ equals the area of the square minus the small square of d^2.

  $8100 - d^2 = 7{,}776$

  Using the "cover method", you find $d^2 = 324$.

  $d = \sqrt{324} = 18$

- The two numbers are $90 + 18$ and $90 - 18$. Check that $108 \times 72 = 7{,}776$.

Babylonian Algebra (3)

If two numbers are added, the result is 150, and if the same numbers are multiplied, the result will be 5,576.

- Find the two numbers using the Babylonian method.

- Find two numbers if you know that the sum is 7 and the product is $8\frac{1}{4}$.

The perimeter of a certain rectangle is 46 m, and the area is 126 m^2.

- Find the length and the width of that rectangle.

Solving quadratic equations: preformal

Historic link

- If the numbers were equal, each of them would be 75.

  But $75 \times 75 = 5{,}625$, and this is larger than 5,576.

  So one of the numbers must be larger than 75, for instance $75 + a$, and the other one must be equally smaller than 75, which is $75 - a$.

  The product of $75 + a$ and $75 - a$ is $5{,}625 - a^2$.

  The product of the two numbers must also be equal to 5,576.

  $5{,}625 - a^2 = 5{,}576$

  $a^2 = 49$

  $a = 7$

  The two numbers are $75 + 7$ and $75 - 7$.
  Check that $82 \times 68 = 5{,}576$.

- If the numbers were equal, each of them would be $3\frac{1}{2}$.

  But $3\frac{1}{2} \times 3\frac{1}{2} = 12\frac{1}{4}$ and this is larger than $8\frac{1}{4}$.

  So one of the numbers must be larger than $3\frac{1}{2}$, for instance $3\frac{1}{2} + a$, and the other one must be equally smaller than $3\frac{1}{2}$, which is $3\frac{1}{2} - a$.

  The product of $3\frac{1}{2} + a$ and $3\frac{1}{2} - a$ is $12\frac{1}{4} - a^2$.

  The product of the two numbers must also be equal to $8\frac{1}{4}$.

  $12\frac{1}{4} - a^2 = 8\frac{1}{4}$

  $a^2 = 4$

  $a = 2$

  The two numbers are $3\frac{1}{2} + 2$ and $3\frac{1}{2} - 2$.
  Check that $5\frac{1}{2} \times 1\frac{1}{2} = 8\frac{1}{4}$.

- You know that adding the lengths of both sides results in 23, and multiplying the sides results in 126.

  If the lengths of the sides were equal, each of them would be $11\frac{1}{2}$.

  But $11\frac{1}{2} \times 11\frac{1}{2} = 132\frac{1}{4}$, and this is larger than 126.

  So one of the numbers must be larger than $11\frac{1}{2}$, for instance $11\frac{1}{2} + a$, and the other one must be equally smaller than $11\frac{1}{2}$, which is $11\frac{1}{2} - a$.

  The product of $11\frac{1}{2} + a$ and $11\frac{1}{2} - a$ is $132\frac{1}{4} - a^2$.

  The product of the two numbers must also be equal to 126.

  $132\frac{1}{4} - a^2 = 126$

  $a^2 = 6\frac{1}{4}$

  $a = 2\frac{1}{2}$

  The two numbers are $11\frac{1}{2} + 2\frac{1}{2}$ and $11\frac{1}{2} - 2\frac{1}{2}$.
  Check that $14 \times 9 = 126$.

Babylonian Algebra (4)

Another Babylonian problem was to calculate two numbers given the difference and the product of those numbers.

Example:

The difference of two numbers is 12, and the product is 189.

<table>
<tr><td align="center">Trial and Error</td><td align="center">Babylonian Method</td></tr>
</table>

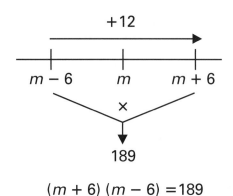

<table>
<tr><td align="center">$a(a + 12) = 189$</td><td align="center">$(m + 6)(m - 6) = 189$</td></tr>
</table>

- Try some values for a, until you find one that works.

- Solve this equation and find both numbers.

Solving quadratic equations: preformal

Historic link

- Note: Even if a trial and error method is used, try to find some smart numbers to work with.

  $10 \times 22 = 220$ too large

  $9 \times 21 = 189$

  The numbers are 9 and 21.

- $(m + 6)(m - 6) = m^2 - 36$

  $m^2 - 36 = 189$

  $m^2 = 225$

  $m = 15$

  The two numbers are $15 + 6 = 21$ and $15 - 6 = 9$.

Patterns and Formulas (1)

A farmer plants apple trees in a square pattern. In order to protect the trees against the wind, he plants conifers all around the orchard.

Here is a diagram of this situation where you can see the pattern of apple trees and conifers for any number (*n*) of rows of apple trees.

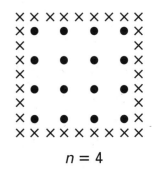

× × ×
× ● ×
× × ×

n = 1

× = conifer
● = apple tree

n = 2

n = 3

n = 4

- How many apple trees does the pattern have when **n = 5**?

  How many conifers does that pattern have?

- Answer the same questions for **n = 10**.

You can use two formulas to calculate the number of apple trees (**A**) and the number of conifers (**C**).

- Complete these formulas.

  A = _____ and **C** = _____

There is a value for **n** for which the number of apple trees equals the number of conifers.

- Find the value of **n** and show your calculations.

There is a value for **n** for which the number of apple trees and conifers together equals 240.

- Find the value of **n**. Show your work.

Use of the relationship between patterns and formulas: formal

Note: Some questions on this page build on the knowledge from page 117, "Equations with Squares."

- For $n = 5$, there are $5 \times 5 = 25$ apple trees and $4 \times 10 = 40$ conifers.

Note that some students may want to draw pattern $n = 5$ and count the number of apple trees and conifers. Other students may start a table. You may wish to discuss different solution strategies here.

- For $n = 10$, there are $10 \times 10 = 100$ apple trees and $4 \times 20 = 80$ conifers.

Sample table that students may have used:

n Pattern Number	Number of Apple Trees	Number of Conifers	Total Number of Apple Trees and Conifers
1	$1 \times 1 = 1$	$4 \times 2 = 8$	$1 + 8 = 9$
2	$2 \times 2 = 4$	$4 \times 4 = 16$	$4 + 16 = 20$
3	$3 \times 3 = 9$	$4 \times 6 = 24$	$9 + 24 = 33$
4	$4 \times 4 = 16$	$4 \times 8 = 32$	$16 + 32 = 48$
5	$5 \times 5 = 25$	$4 \times 10 = 40$	$25 + 40 = 65$
6	$6 \times 6 = 36$	$4 \times 12 = 48$	$36 + 48 = 84$
7	$7 \times 7 = 49$	$4 \times 14 = 56$	$49 + 56 = 105$
8	$8 \times 8 = 64$	$4 \times 16 = 64$	$64 + 64 = 128$
9	$9 \times 9 = 81$	$4 \times 18 = 72$	$81 + 72 = 153$
10	$10 \times 10 = 100$	$4 \times 20 = 80$	$100 + 80 = 180$
n	$n \times n = n^2$	$4 \times 2n$	$n^2 + 8n$

- $A = n \times n$ or $A = n^2$; $C = 4 \times 2n$ or $C = 8n$

- For $n = 8$ the number of apple trees equals the number of conifers. Some students may have drawn this conclusion from their (extended) table. Some may have looked at the equation:

$$n^2 = 8n$$

$$n \times n = 8 \times n$$

and found that solutions for this equation are $n = 0$ (which of course is not possible) and $n = 8$.

- The equation to be solved is $n^2 + 8n = 240$.

Some students, working at an informal level, will extend the table.

Some students may recall the work they did on page 117, "Equations with Squares."

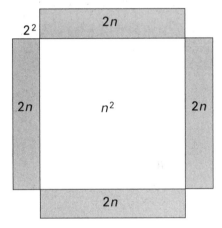

If you "fill up" the small squares of 2×2, a whole square is made with area

$$240 + 4 \times 4 = 256.$$

$256 = 16^2$, so the length of one side of this square is 16.

The length of one side of the square can be expressed as $2 + n + 2$ or $4 + n$.

$$4 + n = 16$$

$$n = 12$$

Have students check that $12^2 + 8 \times 12 = 240$.

Patterns and Formulas (2)

Artist Ivo ten Hove won a contest to design a new tile to be used for sidewalks or patios.

He made a very large X-shaped tile measuring 90 × 90 cm. Here you see a model of this tile.

You can make different square patios with the big tiles and fill the holes with dark gray rectangular tiles as you see in the diagram.

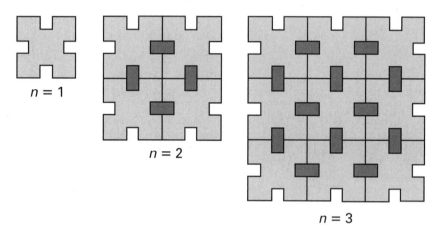

$n = 1$

$n = 2$

$n = 3$

- How many big X-shaped tiles are needed for the pattern with **n = 4**?

  How many dark gray tiles?

- How many big tiles are needed for the pattern with **n = 10**?

  How many dark gray tiles?

B represents the number of big X-shaped tiles, and **G** represents the number of dark gray tiles in a square patio.

- Write an expression with **n** that you can use to compute the number of big tiles.

Helen thinks about a formula to calculate the dark gray tiles.
She thinks this is a good one: **G = 2n² − 2n**

- Is she right? How did she reason?

Peter has found another formula: **G = 2n(n − 1)**

- Is his formula correct? How did he reason?

Use of the relationship between patterns and formulas: formal

Equivalent formulas

Distributive property

- For $n = 4$, there are $4 \times 4 = 16$ big tiles and $4 \times 3 + 3 \times 4 = 24$ dark gray tiles.

  Note that some students may want to draw pattern $n = 4$ and count the number of big tiles and dark gray tiles. Other students may start a table. You may wish to discuss different solution strategies here.

  For $n = 10$, there are $10 \times 10 = 100$ big tiles and $10 \times 9 + 9 \times 10 = 180$ dark gray tiles.

  Sample table that students may have used:

n Patio Number	B Number of Big Tiles	G Number of Dark Gray Tiles
1	$1 \times 1 = 1$	0
2	$2 \times 2 = 4$	$2 \times 2 = 4$
3	$3 \times 3 = 9$	$3 \times 2 + 2 \times 3 = 12$
4	$4 \times 4 = 16$	$4 \times 3 + 3 \times 4 = 24$
5	$5 \times 5 = 25$	$5 \times 4 + 4 \times 5 = 40$
6	$6 \times 6 = 36$	$6 \times 5 + 5 \times 6 = 60$
10	$10 \times 10 = 100$	$10 \times 9 + 9 \times 10 = 180$
n	$n \times n = n^2$	$n(n-1) + (n-1)n$

  Note that it is important for students to see the pattern emerging from the pattern in the drawings as well as the pattern in the numbers in the table to help them make or check a formula.

- Helen is right; the formula is a good one. The formulas $G = 2n(n-1)$ and $G = 2n^2 - 2n$ are equivalent.

- Peter's formula is also right. He may have seen the pattern in the table and rewritten the formula $G = n(n-1) + (n-1)\,n$ as $G = n^2 - n + n^2 - n = 2n^2 - 2n$.

Patterns and Formulas (3)

In a factory, tubes are collected in bundles and bound with steel wire.
The diagram shows the way this is done. Front views are shown.

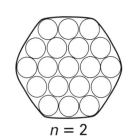

$n = 1$

$n = 2$

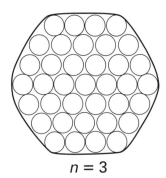

$n = 3$

There is a smart way to count the tubes in each bundle.
Look at the bundle **n = 3**.

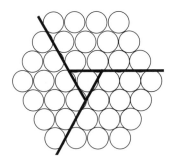

- Fill in the table.

Bundle **n =**	Number of Tubes in Bundle (**T**)
1	7
2	
3	
4	
5	

Rectangular numbers can be used to calculate the number of tubes
in a bundle.

- Explain how.

T is the number of tubes in one collection. **T** can be expressed in **n**.

- Write a formula you can use to compute the number of tubes in
  any bundle.

Use of the relationship between patterns and formulas: formal

Note: Some questions on this page build on the knowledge from pages 77, 78, and 79 "Dot Patterns," Rectangular numbers.

In bundle $n = 3$, you can "see" three rectangular numbers, of 3 by 4.

Sample table. Some students may want to draw bundle $n = 4$ first; look for the rectangular numbers in this bundle: $3 \times (4 \times 5) + 1 = 61$ and check by counting.

n Bundle Number	T Total Number of Tubes in a Bundle
1	7
2	$3 \times (2 \times 3) + 1 = 19$
3	$3 \times (3 \times 4) + 1 = 37$
4	$3 \times (4 \times 5) + 1 = 61$
5	$3 \times (5 \times 6) + 1 = 91$
n	$3 \times (n \times (n + 1)) + 1$

- 2×3 is a rectangular number as is 3×4, 4×5, 5×6, etc.

  In general there are 3 rectangles of dimension $n \times (n + 1)$ in the nth bundle.

- $T = 3 \times (n \times (n + 1)) + 1$ or $T = 3n^2 + 3n + 1$